Target
Get back on track 5

Edexcel GCSE (9–1)
English Literature

An Inspector Calls

Julie Hughes

Pearson

Published by Pearson Education Limited, 80 Strand, London, WC2R ORL.

www.pearsonschoolsandfecolleges.co.uk

Copies of official specifications for all Pearson qualifications may be found on the website: qualifications.pearson.com

Text © Pearson Education Ltd 2017

Typeset by Tech-Set Ltd, Gateshead

The right of Julie Hughes to be identified as author of this work has been asserted by her in accordance with the Copyright, Designs and Patents Act 1988.

First published 2017

20 19 18 17

10 9 8 7 6 5 4 3 2 1

British Library Cataloguing in Publication Data

A catalogue record for this book is available from the British Library

ISBN 978 1 292 23006 1

Printed in Slovakia by Neografia

Acknowledgements

Quotations from An Inspector Calls by J B Priestley (Harlow, UK: Heinemann, 1992) © J B Priestley 1945. Reproduced by permission of Penguin Books Ltd and United Agents on behalf of the Estate of J B Priestley.

Note from the publisher

Pearson has robust editorial processes, including answer and fact checks, to ensure the accuracy of the content in this publication, and every effort is made to ensure this publication is free of errors. We are, however, only human, and occasionally errors do occur. Pearson is not liable for any misunderstandings that arise as a result of errors in this publication, but it is our priority to ensure that the content is accurate. If you spot an error, please do contact us at resourcescorrections@pearson.com so we can make sure it is corrected.

Contents

① Getting the plot straight

This unit will help you to understand and remember the plot of *An Inspector Calls*. The skills you will build are to:

- remember the sequence of key events in the play
- understand the way the plot develops
- select the most significant events for an exam question.

In the exam you will face questions like the ones below. At the end of the unit you will plan your own response to one of these questions.

Exam-style question

Arthur Birling: *Your trouble is – you've been spoilt.*

In what way does Eric change in the play?

You **must** refer to the context of the play in your answer.   **(40 marks)**

Exam-style question

Shelia Birling: *It's you two who are being childish – trying not to face the facts.*

Explore the importance of youth in the play.

You **must** refer to the context of the play in your answer.   **(40 marks)**

Before you tackle these questions, you will work through three key questions in the **skills boosts** to help you get the plot of *An Inspector Calls* straight.

1 How do I make sure I know the plot?

2 How can I explore the development of the play?

3 How do I know which are the most significant events in the play?

Read the start of one student's plan on page 2 for the **second** exam-style question above.

Think about whether the student is: ⊘

using specific events as evidence	showing an understanding of the way the play develops	planning to use the most appropriate events as evidence.

Shelia Birling: *It's you two who are being childish – trying not to face the facts.*

Explore the importance of youth in the play.

You **must** refer to the context of the play in your answer. (40 marks)

Key point	Evidence
1. The older characters are shown as self-satisfied at the start.	• Birling is full of his own importance when the Inspector first arrives: 'I was an alderman for years.' • Birling boasts about his potential knighthood.
2. Mr and Mrs Birling try to dominate the young people.	• Mrs Birling tries to dominate.
3. Young people are shown as shallow, irresponsible and egotistical at the start.	• Sheila is shallow.
4. Youth is shown as capable of change.	• Sheila is shown to change as she becomes strong enough to hear the full story. She insists on being present when Gerald is questioned, despite her mother telling her to leave: 'I wouldn't miss it for worlds.'
5. Youth is shown as becoming responsible – they represent hope.	

(1) The evidence the student uses for key points 2 and 3 is too general. Note down ✐ specific details from the plot that could be added to fully support these key points.

Key point 2: ....

....

Key point 3: ....

....

(2) Underline Ⓐ the key points that show an understanding of the development of the play.

(3) (a) There is no supporting evidence for key point 5. Tick ✓ the sentence below that you think is the most significant event from the play to support this point.

   i Sheila points out when the Inspector leaves that her parents have not learned anything.

   ii Sheila refuses to take part in a toast once the hoax is revealed.

   iii Eric agrees with Sheila that he is frightened by their parents' reaction to the hoax.

(b) Write ✐ **one** sentence explaining your choice.

....

....

How do I make sure I know the plot?

One way to make sure you know the plot of *An Inspector Calls* is to focus on the characters and the part they each played in the death of Eva Smith.

1 Look at this list of characters in the play.

Arthur Birling	Sheila Birling	Edna	Inspector Goole
Mrs Birling	Eric Birling	Gerald Croft	Eva Smith

a Five of the characters listed are questioned by the Inspector. In what order are they questioned? Number them from **1** to **5**.

b Cross out the name of the character who does not actually appear in the play.

c Priestley gives very detailed stage directions at the start of the play. Write **two** sentences explaining how these directions help the audience to see that the Birlings are in a relaxed mood as the play opens.

....

....

2 Read these quotations from Act I.
They all establish the wealth and social position of the Birling family.

a Which quotation best introduces the Birlings' social status?
Tick your choice.

'Tell cook from me'	
'I was Lord Mayor here two years ago'	
'Just a knighthood, of course'	

b Write **one** sentence explaining your choice.

....

....

3 Think about the role played by the Birling and Croft characters in the fate of Eva Smith.
Put this timeline of Eva's life in order by numbering the events **1** to **5** and adding the name of the character responsible for each event.

Order of events	Events	Character responsible
	Eva changes her name to Daisy Renton and starts a relationship with a man. She moves away when he breaks off the relationship.	
	Eva meets a man in Brumley and gets pregnant. He steals money to support her.	
	Eva works at Milwards until she is sacked because of a complaint about her.	
	Eva asks for help from the Brumley Women's Charity but is refused.	
	Eva organises a strike at Birling and Company and is sacked.	

2 How can I explore the development of the play?

One way to explore how the plot of *An Inspector Calls* develops is to consider how Priestley raises and lowers the tension as the characters are questioned about their part in Eva's death.

1 Look at some of the key events from Acts I and II in *An Inspector Calls*.

✎	Act I
	Arthur Birling makes a toast to the engagement.
	Arthur Birling dismisses the idea of a war with Germany.
	The Inspector arrives.
	Sheila runs from the room crying.
	The Inspector leaves with Eric.
	End of Act I: Sheila warns Gerald that the Inspector knows everything.
✎	Act II
	Gerald encourages Sheila to leave.
	Mrs Birling enters, unaware of what has happened.
	Gerald reveals details of his affair with Eva.
	The Inspector reveals that Eva was pregnant.
	Mrs Birling says that the baby's father is entirely to blame.
	Eric enters.

a The tension rises and falls through Acts I and II. Number ✎ the events in each act from **1** to **5**, with **5** being a point of maximum tension for the audience.

b Select **one** of the events you have marked as 5. Write ✎ **one** or **two** sentences explaining how it creates tension for the audience.

....

....

2 At the end of Act III, the tension lightens and the events are carefully developed to create doubt about the Inspector.

a Number ✎ the following events in the correct order (**1** to **4**).

✎	End of Act III
	Mr Birling rings Chief Constable Roberts.
	Sheila questions whether Goole was really an Inspector.
	Gerald rings the infirmary.
	Eric and Mr Birling argue about the stolen money.

b Write ✎ **one** or **two** sentences explaining how the audience would be feeling after event number 4.

....

....

3 How do I know which are the most significant events in the play?

What makes an event or speech significant in *An Inspector Calls* will depend on the focus of the question you are answering.

① Look at these key events from Act I, which can all be linked to the idea of youth in the play.

a Match each event to the correct explanation by drawing lines between them.

A Mr Birling lectures Eric and Gerald about the state of the world

B Eric suddenly bursts out laughing

C Sheila apologises to her father for not listening

a Shows he is immature and slightly drunk, which is disrespectful

b Suggests she is an obedient daughter, which is a traditional role for young women

c Shows he is in charge and feels that younger people should listen to the experience of their elders

b Which event do you think is most significant? Number them **1** to **3**, with **1** being the most significant.

② The events below, from later in the play, can also be linked to the idea of youth.

Mrs Birling is shocked when she hears Eric regularly drinks too much.

Eric challenges his father by suggesting the girls were right to go on strike.

Eric is aggressive towards his mother, accusing her of killing his unborn child.

Eric shows distress and shame over his part in Eva's fate.

a Which event do you think is the most significant? Number them from **1** to **4**, with **1** being most significant.

b Write **one** sentence explaining the link between youth and the event you numbered 1.

....

....

③ Look again at the events from later in the play in question **②**. They can also be linked to the question about how Eric changes.

a Which do you think is the most significant event for a question about Eric changing? Label them **A** to **D**, with **A** being most significant.

b Write **two** sentences explaining what your most significant chosen event suggests about the way Eric changes.

....

....

....

Getting the plot straight

To be sure of writing an effective response about *An Inspector Calls*, you need to:
- know the key events in the play and the order in which they happen
- understand how the plot is developed to create tension
- understand how to select the most significant events for a question.

Look again at this exam-style question from the start of the unit.

Exam-style question

In what way does Eric change in the play?

Look at one student's planning notes in response to this question.

> Eric is first presented as immature.
> - He is described in the stage directions as 'not quite at ease'.
> - He is slightly drunk and suddenly bursts out laughing for no reason [gives hint to audience that he might be an unpredictable character].
> - He interrupts his father [creates tension for audience].
>
> Eric challenges traditional values in Act I.
> - He challenges his father about Birling's sacking of Eva.
> - He shows sympathy for Eva and suggests girls like her should be able to try for higher wages [this hints to audience that he might change].
>
> [Eric off stage for Act II – allows tension to build about his part in Eva's fate. Returns at start of Act III and is last to be questioned – would suggest to audience that his part in her fate is important.]
>
> Eric starts to show remorse/take responsibility.
> - He admits he treated Eva badly and exploited her sexually.
> - He admits he stole money for her.
> - He expresses regret that he couldn't help Eva more.
>
> Eric has changed by end of play.
> - He agrees with Sheila that their parents' reaction is frightening – suggests to audience that he is capable of changing.

(1) Think about all the ideas this student has included in their plan. Annotate ✎ the plan, highlighting and labelling all the different elements that will make the student's response successful.

Your turn!

You are now going to **make planning notes** for the other exam-style question you saw at the beginning of this unit by selecting appropriate plot details.

Exam-style question

> **Shelia Birling:** *It's you two who are being childish – trying not to face the facts.*
>
> Explore the importance of youth in the play.
>
> You **must** refer to the context of the play in your answer. (40 marks)

1 Put these plot details in the correct order by numbering ✐ them from **1** to **10**.

Sheila tells her father not to interfere in her engagement.

Mr Birling is told Eva has killed herself using bleach.

Eric agrees with Sheila that their parents' reaction is frightening.

Mr Birling relaxes when the Inspector has gone and pours drinks.

Mrs Birling tells Sheila not to contradict her.

Eric is drunk at the celebratory party.

Gerald tries to give back the engagement ring.

Sheila accuses her parents of being childish by not facing facts.

Mrs Birling insists the father of the unborn child is to blame.

Mr Birling calls the *Titanic* 'unsinkable'.

2 Which of the plot details above are not relevant to the question? Put a cross ⊗ by them.

3 Which of the plot details suggest that young people represent hope at the end of the play? Circle Ⓐ them and add ✐ appropriate quotations underneath.

4 Which **three** plot details are the most significant for this question? Tick ✓ them.

5 Select **one** of the details you identified in question **4** and write ✐ **two** sentences explaining why it is significant.

....

....

Review your skills

Check up

Review your planning notes for the exam-style question on page 7. Tick ✓ the column to show how well you think you have done each of the following.

	Not quite ✓	Nearly there ✓	Got it! ✓
shown an understanding of the sequence of events in the play	☐	☐	☐
shown an understanding of the development of the play	☐	☐	☐
selected the most significant plot details to explore the theme of youth in the play	☐	☐	☐

Look over all of your work in this unit. Note down ✏ **three** points to remember when considering the plot of *An Inspector Calls*.

1. ....

2. ....

3. ....

Need more practice?

Here is another exam-style question for you to try.

Exam-style question

Eric: *I wasn't in love with her or anything.*

Explore the ideas about love in *An Inspector Calls*?

You **must** refer to the context of the novel in your answer.   (40 marks)

Start by noting down ✏ which plot details from the play you would choose to write about in your response to this question.

How confident do you feel about each of these **skills?** Colour ✏ in the bars.

1 How do I make sure I know the plot?

2 How can I explore the development of the play?

3 How do I know which are the most significant events in the play?

② Exploring character

This unit will help you to understand how characters are presented in *An Inspector Calls* and how to develop your response to them. The skills you will build are to:

- understand the presentation of characters in the play
- explore the development of characters in the play
- link characters to the themes of the play.

In the exam you will face questions like the ones below. At the end of the unit you will plan and write one or two paragraphs in response to one of these questions.

Exam-style question

Sheila: *Between us we drove that girl to suicide.*

How does Sheila change throughout the play?

You **must** refer to the context of the play in your answer.   **(40 marks)**

Exam-style question

Arthur Birling: *A man has to mind his own business and look after himself.*

How is Arthur Birling presented throughout the play?

You **must** refer to the context of the play in your answer.   **(40 marks)**

Before you tackle these questions, you will work through three key questions in the **skills boosts** to help you explore the play's characters.

| **1** How do I make sure I know the characters? | **2** How do I track the development of a character? | **3** How do I link characters to themes? |

Read one student's notes on page 10 on the **second** exam-style question above.

As you read these notes, think about how the student tries to understand the character of Arthur Birling. Has the student: ⊘

shown an understanding of how Arthur Birling is presented	shown an understanding of how his character is developed	selected relevant events and speeches to comment on?

Arthur Birling: *A man has to mind his own business and look after himself.*

How is Arthur Birling presented throughout the play?

You **must** refer to the context of the play in your answer. (40 marks)

Getting to know Arthur Birling and how he uses power	
My ideas	Evidence
At start of play, he is: • self-satisfied • confident • greedy • powerful.	• Boasts about knighthood • Sits symbolically at one end of table • Has most lines before Inspector turns up • Lectures Gerald and Eric, calls them 'youngsters'
As play develops, he becomes: • arrogant – misuses his power • callous – misuses his power.	• Assumes Inspector will feel inferior to his status • Shows no guilt about Eva; calls her 'that girl'
At the end – power shown to be dangerous He is: • dishonest • selfish • cruel.	• Wants to cover up theft of money • Cares more about public scandal than Eva's life • When Inspector goes he jokes about the events and says they will end up laughing about it.
At the end of the play he is unchanged – still feels powerful.	

(1) Which piece of evidence best supports the student's idea that Arthur starts the play as a powerful man? Write (✎) **one** sentence explaining your choice.

....

....

(2) The student has decided that Arthur Birling remains unchanged. Which of the events used as evidence best supports this point? Write (✎) **one** sentence explaining your choice.

....

....

(3) The question is about the theme of power. Which of the following other themes could be linked to the student's point about Arthur Birling's confidence? Tick (✓) your choice(s).

responsibility		reputation		inequality	

1 How do I make sure I know the characters?

To write effectively about characters it is helpful to look at the start of *An Inspector Calls*. This is the point at which characters are established for the audience. You should also consider the stage directions.

(1) Think about how the character of Sheila is presented at the start of the play. In Act I Sheila is described as:

> 'very pleased with life and rather excited'

> talking 'gaily, possessively' to Gerald

> so busy admiring her engagement ring she stops listening to her father

> 'attentive' to her father after apologising for not listening

How would you sum up the character of Sheila in Act I? Tick ✓ any of the words below and/or add ✏ your own ideas.

| shallow | | immature | | sheltered | | | |
| obedient | | traditional | | | | | |

(2) Now think about how the Inspector is presented to the audience when he first appears in Act I.

> described as projecting an 'impression of massiveness'

> the lights get brighter and harder when he arrives

> cuts into Mr Birling's impatient question about why he is there

> looks hard at those he questions

How would you sum up the character of the Inspector in Act I? Tick ✓ any of the words below and/or add ✏ your own ideas.

| powerful | | confident | | unimpressed | | | |
| impatient | | commanding | | | | | |

(3) Think about how the characters in *An Inspector Calls* first respond to the news in Act I that Eva Smith has died from drinking bleach.

> Mr Birling says he doesn't understand why the Inspector has called on his family

> Eric: 'My God!'

> Sheila: 'Oh – how horrible! Was it an accident?'

> Gerald suggests that Mr Birling would rather he wasn't present for the questioning

How would you sum up their reactions? Select **one** word from below for each character or add ✏ one of your own.

> arrogant   uncaring   shocked   sympathetic   indifferent   callous

| Mr Birling | | Eric | |
| Sheila | | Gerald | |

2 How do I track the development of a character?

The plot of *An Inspector Calls* hinges on how characters react to the news about Eva Smith and whether they change as a result of what they hear about her fate. To track a character's development, think about how they respond to the news about Eva throughout the play.

(1) Think about how Sheila is presented at key moments in the play.

| Act I | Wishes she hadn't been told about Eva's death |

| Act I | Shows remorse for treating Eva badly |

| Act II | Warns her mother that the Inspector knows everything |

| Act II | Admits she got Eva sacked but finds it hard to accept responsibility for her death |

| Act III | After Inspector goes, criticises parents for not changing |

| Act III | Remembers the Inspector's warnings and is frightened |

a Circle Ⓐ the **three** most significant moments that suggest a change in Sheila's character.

b Complete 🖉 these **two** sentences summing up how Sheila's character changes during the course of the play.

Sheila's initial reaction to the news about Eva is sympathy, but she soon wishes she hadn't been told. This suggests ....

However, by the end of the play ....

....

(2) The Birling family and Gerald all played a part in Eva's death but by the end of the play only some of them have been changed by what they have heard. Add 🖉 the characters', names along the scale to show how they have changed at the end of the play.

no change   slight remorse   some remorse   extreme remorse

....

(3) Consider how the Inspector remains mysterious throughout the play. Look at these events from Acts II and III.

| Act II | The Inspector comments that 'we often' make an impression on the young ones. |

| Act II | The Inspector shows the photograph to Mrs Birling, then takes it back. |

| Act III | It is revealed that there is no Inspector Goole on the police force. |

Use one of these events to write 🖉 **one** sentence explaining how it makes the Inspector appear mysterious.

....

....

3 How do I link characters to themes?

Priestley uses the character of the Inspector to force the Birling family and Gerald Croft to examine their behaviour. This allows the audience to think about right and wrong in society. When writing your responses, it is a good idea to consider how characters can be linked – through their actions and words – to these key ideas, or themes.

1. Responsibility is one of the key themes of *An Inspector Calls*. Complete 🖉 these notes to show how Priestley uses characters to give audiences ideas about this theme.

Act I: Inspector *says that people should put themselves in the position of girls like Eva.*	Introduces idea of social responsibility
Act I: Mr Birling *says that you need to treat the working class harshly or they will be 'asking for the earth'*	Represents wealthy middle class. Has no social responsibility. Feels...
Act II: Sybil Birling *says that Eva did not seem to be a deserving case for her charity.*	
Act I: Sheila Birling *admits that she used her social status to get Eva dismissed from Milwards.*	

2. Priestley uses the character of Sheila to show how people can develop a sense of responsibility.

   a. Which of the following quotations best shows that Sheila develops a sense of social responsibility over the course of the play? Tick ✓ your choice.

Act III	'Between us we drove that girl to commit suicide'	☐
Act III	'I had her turned out of a job'	☐
Act III	'So there's nothing to be sorry for, nothing to learn …'	☐

   b. Write 🖉 **one** sentence explaining your choice.

   ....

3. Look at the key events involving Arthur Birling, then look at the themes below. Beside each event, write 🖉 the theme that links to it.

Act I	Arthur tells Sybil to thank 'cook'.	☐
Act I	Arthur expresses regret that Gerald's parents can't be at the party.	☐
Act III	Arthur worries that he will lose his chance of a knighthood.	☐

   | reputation   love   equality   age |

Exploring character

To explore how the characters are presented in *An Inspector Calls* you need to:

- think about how they are described and what they say at the start of the play
- consider how they react to the Inspector and whether they change as a result
- link them to themes of the play.

Look again at this exam-style question from the start of the unit.

Exam-style question

How does Sheila change throughout the play?

Look at these two paragraphs from a student's response to this question.

At the start of the play, Priestley presents Sheila as rather shallow. She is described mainly in terms of her appearance, as a 'pretty girl'. She appears to be more interested in admiring her engagement ring than in listening to her father talk about serious issues. She is also presented as very traditional: she is obedient to her father as she apologises for her lack of attention; and she calls her parents 'Mummy' and 'Daddy'.

However, Priestley gives the audience early hints that Sheila may change. She upsets her mother's rather snobbish values as the first of the family to show any sadness about the death of Eva, although her initial reaction is still rather shallow as she thinks of it in terms of the way it has spoiled her evening, declaring 'I wish you hadn't told me.' As the interrogation of Arthur Birling progresses, her interest in what happened to Eva intensifies and she begins to challenge her father, by 'cutting in' when he is trying to placate the Inspector. Her emerging sense of responsibility then becomes evident as she tells her father that sacking Eva was a 'mean' thing to do.

1 **a** Underline (A) any phrases in the first paragraph that show this student understands how Sheila is presented at the start of the play. Label them '**Presentation**'.

  b Highlight in green where the student has shown understanding of how Sheila's character develops throughout the play. Label them '**Development**'.

  c Highlight in yellow links the student has made to the themes of social class and responsibility. Label them '**Themes**'.

2 Which of the following themes could also be linked to Sheila in these paragraphs? Annotate the student's response with your ideas.

> age   reputation   power   equality

Your turn!

You are now going to **write your own two paragraphs** in response to one of the exam-style questions.

Exam-style question

Sheila: *Between us we drove that girl to suicide.*

How does Sheila change throughout the play?

You **must** refer to the context of the play in your answer. (40 marks)

Complete these tasks to make notes for your answer.

(1) Gather notes ✏ about how Sheila is presented at the start of the play, up until the Inspector arrives. Remember to consider stage directions.

....

....

....

....

(2) Gather notes ✏ about how Sheila's character develops in Acts I and II. Remember to consider how her reaction to Eva's fate suggests she will change.

....

....

....

....

(3) Gather notes ✏ about how Sheila is presented in Act III. Consider how the audience is shown that she is the character who changes the most.

....

....

....

....

(4) **a** Go back over your notes and make further notes ✏ on the following themes, and/or your own themes.

| age | social responsibility | equality |

....

....

b Use your planning notes to write ✏ **two** paragraphs on paper in response to the exam-style question above.

Review your skills

Check up

Review your response to the exam-style question on page 15. Tick ✓ the column to show how well you think you have done each of the following.

	Not quite ✓	Nearly there ✓	Got it! ✓
shown an understanding of how Sheila is presented at key points in the play	☐	☐	☐
shown an understanding of how Sheila's character develops throughout the play	☐	☐	☐
linked Sheila's character to key themes in the play	☐	☐	☐

Look over all of your work in this unit. Note down ✐ **three** important things to remember when exploring the presentation of a character in *An Inspector Calls*.

1. ....

2. ....

3. ....

Need more practice?

Try writing ✐ **two** paragraphs of an answer to the **second** question you saw on page 9.

Exam-style question

Arthur Birling: *A man has to mind his own business and look after himself.*

How is Arthur Birling presented throughout the play?

You **must** refer to the context of the play in your answer.   (40 marks)

Think about:
- how Arthur Birling is presented at the start of the play, including stage directions
- how he reacts to the Inspector's questioning and to Eva's fate
- how he can be linked to power and any other themes.

How confident do you feel about each of these **skills?** Colour ✐ in the bars.

1 How do I make sure I know the characters?

2 How do I track the development of a character?

3 How do I link characters to themes?

③ Exploring themes

This unit will help you to understand and explore how the themes of *An Inspector Calls* are presented in the play. The skills you will build are to:

- identify the themes in the play
- comment on the development of themes in the play
- link themes to character, setting and structure.

In the exam you will face questions like the one below. At the end of the unit you will plan and write one or two paragraphs in response to this question.

> **Exam-style question**
>
> **Arthur Birling:** *A man has to mind his own business and look after himself.*
>
> Explore the significance of responsibility in the play.
>
> You **must** refer to the context of the play in your answer.   (40 marks)

Before you tackle this question, you will work through three key questions in the **skills boosts** to help you explore the themes in *An Inspector Calls*.

| ① How do I identify the themes of the play? | ② How do I track the development of a theme? | ③ How do I link themes to character, setting and plot? |

Look at one student's notes for this exam-style question on page 18.

As you read these notes, think about whether the student has:

| shown an understanding of the way responsibility is shown in the play | tracked and commented on the development of responsibility in the play | linked responsibility to appropriate characters, settings and plot details. |

Explore the significance of responsibility in the play.

Introduction	• Priestley presents responsibility as significant.
	• He uses the play to show that people in society should take responsibility for those who are less fortunate.
Responsibility presented as lacking in higher classes	• Mr Birling makes speech at start about man having to look after himself.
	• Mr and Mrs Birling don't change.
Inspector used to show significance of responsibility	• He says: 'We don't live alone. We are members of one body. We are responsible for each other.' (Act I)
Inspector questions each character in turn to build a picture of how they showed no responsibility for Eva	• Mr Birling sacked her and calls her 'that girl'. (Act I) • Sheila had her dismissed. (Act I) • Mrs Birling refused to help her. (Act II)
Sheila and Eric start to take responsibility for their actions	• Sheila shows guilt when questioned: 'I'll never, never do it again.' (Act I) • Eric says: 'the girl's dead and we all helped to kill her'. (Act III) • Suggests young people will start to take responsibility – they are the hope for the future.

(1) Underline (A) where the student has shown an understanding of how the Inspector is used to present ideas about responsibility.

(2) Circle (A) where the student has tracked the development of the theme of responsibility. Label (✏) these sections '**development**'.

(3) Annotate (✏) your plan with one of your own ideas about how responsibility is presented in the play.

1 How do I identify the themes of the play?

In *An Inspector Calls* Priestley raises some of his key ideas about how people should live. These key ideas are called 'themes' and it is important that you can identify them in your responses. To do this, start by considering Eva's story. First, think about the ideas it presents to the audience. Then go on to consider key events in the play.

① Look at some of the key themes from *An Inspector Calls* and key events in Eva's story.

A Responsibility	a Eva is sacked for organising a strike at the factory.
B Morality	b Gerald breaks off his relationship with Eva.
C Power	c Mrs Birling turns Eva away from her charity.
D Equality	d Sheila uses her social status to get Eva dismissed from Milwards.
E Love	e Eva commits suicide.

a What idea does each event raise for the audience? Draw lines to match the events to the themes. Some events may link to more than one theme.

b Select and highlight **one** event. Annotate it with your ideas about how it can be linked to one of the themes.

② Some key points in the play can be linked to more than one theme. Read Arthur Birling's speech from the start of Act I.

> **Birling:** (*solemnly*) But this is the point. I don't want to lecture you two young fellows again. But what so many of you don't seem to understand now, when things are so much easier, is that a man has to make his own way – has to look after himself – and his family too, of course, when he has one – and so long as he does that he won't come to much harm. But the way some of these cranks talk and write now, you'd think everybody has to look after everybody else, as if we were all mixed up together like bees in a hive – community and all that nonsense. But take my word for it, you youngsters – and I've learnt in the good hard school of experience – that a man has to mind his own business and look after himself and his own …

a Tick any of the themes below that can be linked to Birling's speech.

responsibility		morality		power		equality	

b For **two** of the themes, annotate the speech to explain the links you have made.

2 How do I track the development of a theme?

You can explore how themes develop in *An Inspector Calls* by considering how they are presented in different parts of the play.

(1) Look at some of the key events in Act I, where Priestley introduces the idea of power.

> Arthur Birling talks about employers coming together to protect their interests.

> Arthur Birling tells the Inspector that he used to be Lord Mayor.

> Arthur Birling tells the Inspector he told the strikers to 'clear out'.

> The Inspector accuses Sheila of using her power as a valued customer to get Eva dismissed.

a How does Priestley present power in this act of the play? Tick ✓ any of the ideas below.

	as belonging to the middle classes		as dangerous		as positive
	as corrupting		as necessary		as taken for granted		as negative

b Write ✎ a sentence explaining **one** of your ideas.

....

....

(2) Now consider these two statements about how power is presented later in the play.

Statement 1

> The power shifts from Mr and Mrs Birling to the Inspector.

Statement 2

> The power shifts from Arthur and Sybil Birling to their children.

a Tick ✓ any of the events below you think are most relevant as evidence for **Statement 1**.

	Key event 1		**Key event 2**		**Key event 3**
	Act III: The Inspector tells Arthur to 'stop'. He is described as 'taking charge masterfully', with other characters falling silent.		Act III: Arthur pours himself a drink as soon as the Inspector has left.		Act III: The telephone interrupts Arthur when he is saying that the younger generation can't take a joke.

b For **Statement 2**, write ✎ **one** sentence explaining what Priestley wants the audience to feel about power at that point in the play.

....

....

(3) Complete ✎ these sentences to show how the presentation of power changes as the play progresses.

At the start, power is shown to belong to the middle classes when ....

....

However, later in the play, ...

....

3 How do I link themes to character, setting and plot?

When you answer a theme-based question you should select the most significant points from the play as evidence for your ideas. You will also need to think about how Priestley links themes to his characters, the setting and the plot of the play.

1 What does Priestley suggest through his themes? Complete the table 🖊 to show:
   a which characters and themes link together
   b which key event best supports each link.

Theme	Character	Key event
Reputation – shows that it is more important to middle class than taking responsibility for others in society.	Mr Birling	In Act III he is more concerned about a potential scandal than about Eva's fate.
Responsibility – suggests everybody should care for others and think carefully about their actions.		
Equality – shows that a lack of equality makes working class lives very difficult.		

2 Think about the setting of *An Inspector Calls*. Read this extract from the stage directions at the start of the play.

> At rise of curtain, the four BIRLINGS and GERALD are seated at the table, with ARTHUR BIRLING at one end, his wife at the other, ERIC downstage and SHEILA and GERALD seated upstage. EDNA, the parlourmaid, is just clearing the table, which has no cloth, of dessert plates and champagne glasses, etc., and then replacing them with a decanter of port, cigar box and cigarettes. Port glasses are already on the table.

   a Which of the following themes can be linked to this extract? Tick ✓ your choices.

   equality ☐   respectability ☐   power ☐   exploitation ☐   responsibility ☐

   b For **one** of your choices, underline Ⓐ where in the extract the theme is evident.

3 Think about the plot of the play.

   Complete the table 🖊 to show what each stage of Eva's story suggests about responsibility.

Stages of Eva's story	Suggestion about responsibility
Stage 1: Sheila admits she used her social position to get Eva dismissed.	
Stage 2: Gerald says he has no idea what happened to Eva after he broke off their relationship.	
Stage 3: Eric admits he was drunk when he first went to Eva's lodgings.	

Exploring themes

To explore themes in *An Inspector Calls* and write about them effectively in your responses, you need to:

- think about how key scenes and speeches are used to present Priestley's themes
- compare how themes are presented at different points in the play
- consider how characters, the setting and the plot are used to present themes.

Look again at this exam-style question you saw at the start of the unit.

Exam-style question

Arthur Birling: *A man has to mind his own business and look after himself.*

Explore the significance of responsibility in the play.

You **must** refer to the context of the play in your answer. (40 marks)

Look at these two paragraphs written by one student in response to this exam-style question.

At the start of the play, Priestley suggests that the wealthy middle class has no sense of responsibility for others. This is shown through the Birlings, who are presented as wealthy by the comfortable setting and the way the play starts with a celebration of Sheila's engagement. Arthur then shows his lack of responsibility for others by telling Gerald and Eric that men should look after themselves and their families. He calls people who want to look after everybody else 'cranks', which shows he thinks the idea is ridiculous.

Later in Act I, Arthur also shows that he takes no responsibility for the welfare of his workers. When questioned by the Inspector he says his only responsibility is to 'keep labour costs down'. This shows he cares more for money than he does for the people who work in his factory. He is shown as feeling no guilt and taking no responsibility for Eva's fate. Priestley wants the audience to disapprove of Arthur's view as he is presented as callous, calling Eva 'that girl' and referring to his workers as 'these people'.

In contrast, the Inspector ....

....

(**1**) Underline Ⓐ where the student has used key events to support the points made about the theme. Label them ✎ **'key events'**.

(**2**) Circle Ⓐ where the student has linked characters, the setting or the plot of the play to the theme. Label them ✎ **'character'**, **'setting'** or **'plot'**.

(**3**) The student has started a third paragraph about the Inspector. Complete ✎ the opening sentence. Try to show an understanding of how the theme of responsibility is developed through the Inspector.

Your turn!

You are now going to **write your own answer** in response to this exam-style question.

Exam-style question

Arthur Birling: *A man has to mind his own business and look after himself.*

Explore the significance of responsibility in the play.

You **must** refer to the context of the play in your answer. (40 marks)

You should spend around 30 minutes on this type of question, so you should aim to write **four** or **five** paragraphs.

1 Use the table below to note down how responsibility is shown in all three acts of *An Inspector Calls*. Select **two** key events from each act.

	Act I	Act II	Act III
Key event 1			
Key event 2			

2 Look carefully at the events you have chosen. Do they highlight how the theme of responsibility is shown in different ways at different points in the play? Add notes to your ideas about how the theme is developed.

3 Think about characters and the setting of the play. Add notes to show how these are used to present different ideas about responsibility.

4 Use your notes to write **two** paragraphs on paper in response to this question.

Review your skills

Check up

Review your response to the exam-style question on page 23. Tick ✓ the column to show how well you think you have done each of the following.

	Not quite ✓	Nearly there ✓	Got it! ✓
identified key events or speeches where the theme of responsibility is presented	☐	☐	☐
commented on how the theme of responsibility is developed	☐	☐	☐
linked ideas about responsibility to characters and the setting of the play	☐	☐	☐

Look over all of your work in this unit. Note down ✏ **three** points to remember when writing about themes in *An Inspector Calls*.

1. ....

2. ....

3. ....

Need more practice?

Here is another exam-style question, this time exploring the theme of power.

Exam-style question

Arthur Birling: *I was an alderman for years – and Lord Mayor.*

Explore the significance of power in the play.

You **must** refer to the context of the play in your answer.   (40 marks)

Plan and write ✏ a response to this question.

Remember to think about how the theme is developed and whether it can be linked to any characters or the setting of the play.

How confident do you feel about each of these **skills?** Colour ✏ in the bars.

1 How do I identify the themes of the play?

2 How do I track the development of a theme?

3 How do I link themes to character, setting and plot?

④ Exploring context

This unit will help you to show your understanding of the play's context – its relationship with the time it was written, the time it was set and the way different audiences respond. The skills you will build are to:

- understand the relationship between the play and its context
- use relevant contextual ideas
- make relevant comments about audience responses.

In the exam you will face questions like the ones below. At the end of the unit you will plan your own response to one of these questions.

Exam-style question

Arthur Birling: *If you don't come down sharply on some of these people, they'd soon be asking for the earth.*

In what ways is social class important in *An Inspector Calls*?

You **must** refer to the context of the play in your answer.   (40 marks)

Exam-style question

Sybil Birling: *In the circumstances I think I was justified.*

Explore the significance of the character of Sybil Birling in the play.

You **must** refer to the context of the play in your answer.   (40 marks)

Before you tackle these questions, you will work through three key questions in the **skills boosts** to help you explore the context of *An Inspector Calls*.

 ① How do I make sure I know the context?   **② How do I select relevant contextual ideas?**   **③ How do I include ideas about audience response?**

Read part of one student's notes on page 26 on the **first** exam-style question above.

Think about whether the student has: ⊘

shown an understanding of the context of the play

planned to use relevant contextual ideas

shown an understanding of different audience responses.

In what ways is social class important in *An Inspector Calls*?

Start of play: Priestley makes the difference in class immediately obvious – shows this is an important theme	• *Setting is a comfortable house, Birlings and Gerald sitting and in evening dress* • *Contrast to Edna who is silently clearing the table* • *Represents division of classes at the time*
Arthur Birling shows distrust of working classes	• *Says working classes should be treated harshly* • *Links to labour strikes of time play is set, when wealthy middle classes worried that spread of socialism would mean losing what they had* • *Gerald agrees – suggests view was common at the time*
Sybil looks down on working classes	• *Refers to Eva as 'that sort' when hearing about her relationship with Eric* • *Reflects view at the time that working classes had lower moral standards*

(1) Underline (A) where the student has shown an understanding of the context of the play.

(2) What point do you think Priestley was making about social class at the time the play was set? Write (✎) **one** or **two** sentences to explain your ideas.

....

....

....

(3) The student has not planned any comments on audience response. Select **one** of the points above and annotate (✎) it with your ideas about how a modern audience would respond.

How do I make sure I know the context?

You need to be aware of all the different contexts of *An Inspector Calls* so you can make relevant comments in your responses. Contextual ideas can be historical events, or relevant beliefs and attitudes from the time the play was written and set. To help you remember key contextual ideas, you can link them to characters and themes.

(1) Look at these contextual ideas from *An Inspector Calls*. Tick ✓ any that are relevant to the play.

✓	Contextual ideas, 1912	Characters, links to context and themes
	Titanic sunk in April	
	No unemployment benefits	
	Position in society very important to Edwardians	*Arthur Birling; more concerned about reputation than Eva's fate*
	Coal miners' strike secured minimum wage	
	Women paid less than men for same job	
	Most married women were dependent on their husbands	
	J.B. Priestley went to university	
	Captain Scott died in the Antarctic	
	Suffragettes were protesting for the vote	

(2) Characters and themes can be linked to relevant contextual ideas. For example:

Arthur Birling ➡ position in society very important ➡ *Arthur is more concerned about his reputation than about Eva.*

Think about the characters and themes below. Link them to the contextual ideas you ticked in question **(1)** by writing 🖉 **one** character or **one** theme next to each idea and explaining the link.

Eva Smith	Arthur Birling	Sybil Birling	Gerald	Sheila

equality	reputation	power	responsibility	social class

(3) The play is set in 1912 but was written and first performed in 1945. Look again at the ideas above and think about what happened in Britain between these two dates.

On paper, make notes 🖉 about how life have been different for Eva and Sheila in 1945.

> Think about the way all social classes fought together in the war; how women replaced men in the workplace and won the vote in 1918; and how the welfare state was established in 1945.

2 How do I select relevant contextual ideas?

You do not need to make contextual comments in every paragraph of your response, but any comments you *do* make must be relevant to the point you are making.

1. Read what one student wrote in answer to the **first** exam-style question about Arthur Birling on page 25.

> Arthur Birling is presented as callous. This is shown in Act I when he is being questioned about Eva's part in the strike and he talks about the need to treat his workers harshly. This shows he cares more about profits than about the workers in his factory.

a. Which contextual ideas best support this point? Tick ✓ your choice.

☐ *Titanic* sunk in April 1912	☐ No unemployment benefits in 1912	☐ 1912 coal miners' strike secured minimum wage

b. Write ✏ **one** sentence explaining your choice.

....

....

2. Look at one student's notes about Sybil Birling.

defer: let someone else decide

> • Sybil comes from a higher social position than Arthur, but she usually **defers** to him. This is shown when he asks her to pass on a message to 'cook' about the meal.
>
> • Sybil is shown to be naïve about her children. She is shocked when she finds out in Act II that Eric has an alcohol problem.
>
> • Sybil takes no responsibility for her actions. She will not take any blame for refusing to help Eva and says that her decision to turn her away was entirely justified.

a. Underline Ⓐ any points that link Sybil to contextual ideas about life for women in 1912.

b. Write ✏ **one** sentence explaining your choice.

....

....

3. What other contextual ideas might be relevant for the **second** exam-style question on page 25 about Sybil Birling? Make notes ✏ below using the ideas from this page and any other ideas you might have.

....

....

....

....

....

....

3 How do I include ideas about audience response?

An effective comment on the context of *An Inspector Calls* should focus on relevant beliefs and attitudes that are reflected in the play. One way to do this is to consider the impact of the play on Priestley's audience, and the way a modern audience's response might differ.

① Look at the beginning of one student's paragraph in response to the **second** question on page 25 (about Sybil).

Exam-style question

Explore the significance of the character of Sybil Birling in the play.

> In Act I Sybil Birling warns Sheila that when she is married she will have to take second place as men 'spend nearly all their time and energy' on business.

A This presentation of Sybil is typical of married women at the time the play was written as they were expected to stay at home even though they could vote and work. Twenty-first century women in the audience would find it difficult to sympathise with her as they expect more independence and do not feel the need to defer to men.

B This acceptance of a subservient role would not have surprised Priestley's audience in 1945. Despite advances, such as women getting the vote and taking on valuable roles in WWI, the majority of women at that time would have deferred to their husbands. To a twenty-first century audience, however, Sybil might appear to be weak and shallow as modern women expect to be independent even when married.

C To an audience in 1945, Sybil would seem typical of the middle class but modern audiences would find it difficult to accept that she stayed at home and allowed her husband to take charge.

a For each point below, circle Ⓐ any paragraphs that match and cross out ~~cat~~ any that don't. Two examples have already been started.

  a Identifies the time the play was written   A Ⓑ C

  b Identifies a relevant belief or attitude at that time   A B C

  c Considers changing beliefs and attitudes   A B C

  d Identifies relevant historical events or issues   A B ~~C~~

  e Compares a twentieth-century audience with a twenty-first century audience A B C

b Which of the three paragraphs would you use when writing about Sybil Birling? Tick ✓ **one or more**.

② How would different audiences respond to Sybil refusing charity to Eva? Write 🖉 **two** sentences explaining:

- how an audience in 1945 would feel about Eva at this point
- how beliefs and attitudes have changed since 1945
- how these changes might affect a modern audience's feelings about Sybil's actions.

....

....

....

Exploring context

To show an understanding of the context of *An Inspector Calls* you need to:
- identify the relationship between the play and its context
- use the most relevant contextual ideas in your responses
- consider the changes in audience response since the play was written.

Look again at this exam-style question from the start of the unit.

Exam-style question

Sybil Birling: *In the circumstances I think I was justified.*

Explore the significance of the character of Sybil Birling in the play.

You **must** refer to the context of the play in your answer. (40 marks)

Look at these two paragraphs from one student's response.

Priestley presents Sybil as feeling no sense of responsibility towards the lower classes. She pays no attention to her servant, Edna, unless it is to give her orders and shows no concern for her welfare as she tells her to wait up until she is needed. This reflects Priestley's negative feelings about the way the rich in Edwardian society treated the working classes.

Sybil accepts no blame for her part in Eva's death. She is presented as very judgemental, calling Eva a girl 'of that class' and looking down on her for being single and pregnant. Despite sitting on a charitable committee, she only helps those she feels have earned it, and feels Eva was herself to blame. Beliefs about the working class had begun to change in 1945, with the introduction of the welfare state, so an audience at that time would have been more sympathetic than Sybil about Eva's situation. A twenty-first century audience would certainly feel Sybil's attitude was wrong and might even see her as cruel.

- makes a clear point about Sybil, linking her to the theme of responsibility

- uses a key event or speech as evidence

- identifies a relevant contextual idea

- comments on audience at the time the play was written

- compares 1945 audience with modern audience response

(1) Link each point ✏ on the right to the place in the student paragraphs where it is covered and underline Ⓐ all the relevant words.

Your turn!

You are now going to **write your own answer** in response to the exam-style question below.

Exam-style question

Sybil Birling: *In the circumstances I think I was justified.*

Explore the significance of the character of Sybil Birling in the play.

You **must** refer to the context of the play in your answer. **(40 marks)**

(1) Before you start your response, identify **three** points about Sybil Birling's presentation in the play. Expand them ✐ using the prompts below.

> Point 1:
>
> Point 2:
>
> Point 3:

Prompt 1: Which key events can you use as evidence? Add relevant events or speeches to your points above.

Prompt 2: Think about any relevant contextual ideas and add them to your points above.

Prompt 3: Think about different audience responses. Would a modern audience respond differently from an audience at the time the play was written? How would responses reflect the attitudes and beliefs of different audiences? Add your ideas to your points above.

(2) Use your planning notes to write ✐ your response to the exam-style question above on paper.

Review your skills

Check up

Review your response to the exam-style question on page 31. Tick ✓ the column to show how well you think you have done each of the following.

	Not quite ✓	Nearly there ✓	Got it! ✓
identified links between the play and the context	☐	☐	☐
used the most relevant contextual ideas	☐	☐	☐
commented on different audience responses to the play	☐	☐	☐

Look over all of your work in this unit. Note down ✐ **three** points to remember when commenting on context in *An Inspector Calls*.

1. ....

2. ....

3. ....

Need more practice?

Here is another exam-style question for you to try.

Exam-style question

Arthur Birling: *If you don't come down sharply on some of these people, they'd soon be asking for the earth.*

In what ways is social class important in *An Inspector Calls*?

You **must** refer to the context of the play in your answer. (40 marks)

Plan and write ✐ a response to this question.

Remember to only add contextual ideas that are relevant to the point you are making.

How confident do you feel about each of these **skills?** Colour ✐ in the bars.

1 How do I make sure I know the context?

2 How do I select relevant contextual ideas?

3 How do I include ideas about audience response?

⑤ Unlocking the question

This unit will help you to understand the questions you will need to answer on *An Inspector Calls*. The skills you will build are to:

- choose the right question
- unlock the requirements of the question
- develop a critical judgement in response to the focus of the question.

In the exam you will face questions like the ones below. At the end of the unit you will write part of a response to one of these questions.

Exam-style question

Sybil Birling: *But I accept no blame for it at all.*

How are ideas about guilt important in *An Inspector Calls*?

You **must** refer to the context of the play in your answer.   (40 marks)

Exam-style question

Sheila: *You and I aren't the same people who sat down to dinner here.*

Explore the relationship between Sheila and Gerald.

You **must** refer to the context of the play in your answer.   (40 marks)

Before you tackle these questions, you will work through three key questions in the **skills boosts** to help you unlock exam questions.

| **1** How do I choose a question? | **2** How do I unlock the question? | **3** How do I develop a critical judgement? |

Look at one student's notes on page 34 on the **first** exam-style question above.

As you read the notes, think about whether the student has:

linked points to plot/setting/ character and context

shown an understanding of the focus of the question

made a critical judgement in response to the focus of the question.

Sybil Birling: *But I accept no blame for it at all.*

How are ideas about guilt important in *An Inspector Calls*?

You **must** refer to the context of the play in your answer.

(40 marks)

Guilt – important theme as it makes characters face responsibility (Priestley's main idea in play)

Guilt introduced by Inspector:

• *when bell rings they are celebrating – they joke it might be something Eric's done – typical Edwardian wealthy middle class, shows how secure they feel about social position*

Characters used to show guilt:

• *Arthur and Sybil show no guilt. In Act I Arthur calls his sacking of Eva justified – reflects treatment of working class at time – modern audience might see this as arrogant and callous*

• *Gerald shows some guilt in Act II – wishes Eva had blamed him; but by end of play he shows double standards as he expects Sheila to take back the engagement ring – reflects gender inequality of 1912 – 1945 audience would accept this*

• *Sheila and Eric show guilt – Sheila self-centred at start (feels she can never go to Milwards again) – at end says they all drove Eva to suicide – youth shown as hope for the future*

Inspector wants each character to take responsibility:

• *Stands for socialist ideas about responsibility – Act III before he leaves he talks about people being responsible for each other and 'members of one body'. – reflects new ideas after WWII*

---

① Has the student used key events or speeches as evidence for each point? Underline Ⓐ **one** of the points where there is a clear link and label 🖉 it '**evidence**'.

② Has the student linked points to the following?

| Themes/setting | Context | Audience response | Structure |

Circle Ⓐ **one** example of each and label 🖉 it '**themes**', '**setting**', '**context**', '**audience**' or '**structure**'.

③ Has the student maintained a close focus on the question? Circle Ⓐ **Yes / No** .

How do I choose a question?

When looking at two questions on the exam paper, it is important to choose the one you can answer most effectively. It is important *not* to choose a question just because you know a lot about a character and their part in the plot of the play. You should aim to choose a question for which you can:

- make clear points that focus on the question
- use key events or speeches as evidence
- make a link to contextual ideas.

Look at one student's initial ideas in response to both exam-style questions on page 33.

Exam-style question

How are ideas about guilt important in
An Inspector Calls?

Exam-style question

Explore the relationship between Sheila and
Gerald.

- Guilt important – links to responsibility
- Sybil and Arthur show traditional view – not guilty – felt justified
- Sheila and Eric represent youth – see their guilt
- Inspector shows importance of guilt
- Link to responsibility for working classes
- Play structured to reveal their guilt slowly

- In love at start
- Sheila cross about Gerald's affair
- Gerald used Eva
- He was kind to Eva
- Gerald had no idea what happened to Eva
- Sheila forgives him
- Gerald tries to give ring back
- Sheila doesn't take it
- Sheila says their relationship has changed

(1) Which plan makes points that focus on the question? Label it 🖋 **'Points'**. The other plan uses key events to tell the story. Label it 🖋 **'Plot'**.

(2) One way to decide if you can write an effective response is to see whether you can link your ideas to key concepts. For example, think about the **second** question on page.

Exam-style question

Sheila: *You and I aren't the same people who sat down to dinner here.*

Explore the relationship between Sheila and Gerald.

| setting | theme | structure | context | audience |

(a) Draw lines 🖋 to link the key ideas to the exam-style question and annotate 🖋 to explain your links.

(b) For **one** of the links you have made, note down 🖋 a key event or speech you could use as evidence.

② How do I unlock the question?

When you have chosen a question, make sure you fully understand what it is asking. To do this, you should think carefully about:

- the words used in the question
- the meaning of the quotation given in the question.

① Some questions may use words or phrases that do not seem immediately obvious to the themes you need to focus on. For example, look at the themes that can be linked to this question.

Exam-style question

Gerald: *This isn't the time to pretend that Eric isn't used to drink.*

Explore the significance of <u>secrets and lies</u> in the play.

responsibility ☐   power ☐

a In the spaces, write 🖉 **two** other themes that can be linked to the idea of 'secrets and lies'.

b List 🖉 **three** characters who would be relevant to this question.

Character 1: ....   Character 2: ....   Character 3: ....

② Look at some other words and phrases that might be used in theme-based questions.

a Link 🖉 the words and phrases on the left with the major themes on the right. Some may link to more than one theme.

b Write 🖉 **one** sentence explaining one of the links you have made.

....
....
....

A exploitation	a responsibility
B relationships	
C conflict	b power
D duty	
E hypocrisy	c equality
F reputation	d morality
G gender roles	
H guilty conscience	e love

③ The quotation given with each question can help you to understand what the question is asking. Annotate 🖉 each exam-style question below, drawing arrows ⤓ linking the quotation with the focus of the question.

a **Exam-style question**

Sybil: *I consider I did my duty.*

Explore the importance of duty in the play.

b **Exam-style question**

Gerald: *What about this ring?*

In what ways is Gerald significant in the play?

③ How do I develop a critical judgement?

Before you plan your written response, you need to make a critical judgement on the topic in the question. To do this you need to:

- weigh up the ideas suggested in the question
- think about Priestley's intentions when he wrote the play.

① Look at this character-based exam-style question.

How is he represented?

What social class does he represent?

Exam-style question

In what ways is <u>Gerald</u> <u>important</u> in the play.

Does he change?

What key themes does this link him to? | power / morality / love

a Complete ✏️ Ⓐ the student's ideas above.

b Use your notes to choose the most appropriate critical judgement. Tick ✓ your choice.

> **A** Gerald is important in the play as he represents the wealthy upper class and is linked to ideas about morals.

> **B** In An Inspector Calls, Priestley uses the character of Gerald to explore ideas about the morality of the upper classes.

> **C** Gerald is important in the play as he is shown to have double standards.

② Now think about how to develop a critical judgement on a theme-based exam-style question.

Why does Priestley include the idea of power in the play?

Does it link to other themes?

Exam-style question

<u>How</u> are the ideas about <u>power shown</u> in An Inspector Calls?

Which characters can be linked to power?

How is power shown? | positive / negative / a bit of both

a Complete ✏️ Ⓐ the student's ideas above.

b Use your answers to write ✏️ **one** or **two** sentences summing up your critical judgement about how and why power is explored in An Inspector Calls.

Unlocking the question

To write an effective response you need to show a full understanding of the focus of the question by:

- choosing the question that allows you to make clear points
- considering the words in the question and using the quotation for ideas
- developing a critical judgement that shows an understanding of Priestley's purpose.

Look again at the **second** exam-style question you saw at the start of the unit.

Exam-style question

Explore the relationship between Sheila and Gerald.

Look at these two paragraphs from the start of one student's response to this exam-style question.

> Sheila begins the play as a rather shallow character. In the stage directions at the start, Priestley describes Sheila in terms of her physical appearance and her excitement about her engagement, which gives the audience an initial impression of a rather frivolous girl. Her excited reaction to the engagement also suggests she is happy to follow the traditional expectations for the daughter of a wealthy family in the early twentieth century and marry somebody who will help the family achieve a higher social status.
>
> However, there are very early signs that Sheila may change. Before the Inspector's arrival she raises suspicions about Gerald's behaviour but does not pursue them, which suggests that she is still too naïve to see beyond the romance of their relationship. She is warned by her mother that wives must come second to their husbands' business interests. This is emphasised when Arthur talks about how much the engagement means to him, suggesting that to him and Gerald it is more of a business arrangement than a love match. This is the first hint in the play that love means different things to men and women.

1 **a** Which of these critical judgements do the paragraphs best support? Tick ✓ your choice.

> **A** Sheila's relationship with Gerald is important in the play as it shows how Sheila changes.

> **B** Priestley uses the relationship between Sheila and Gerald to explore ideas about love and responsibility.

> **C** In *An Inspector Calls* Sheila's relationship with Gerald shows what life was like for a traditional young lady in 1912.

b Underline (A) where the student has made clear points. Label 🖉 them '**Points**'.

c Circle (A) where the student has used key events as evidence. Label 🖉 them '**Evidence**'.

d Identify and label 🖉 any links made to '**key themes**', '**characters**' or '**contextual ideas**'.

Your turn!

You are now going to **write your own response** to the exam-style question below.

Exam-style question

Sybil Birling: *But I accept no blame for it at all.*

How are ideas about guilt important in *An Inspector Calls*?

You **must** refer to the context of the play in your answer. **(40 marks)**

---

1 Weigh up the ideas in the question in order to come up with a critical judgement.

a How is guilt shown? Circle Ⓐ your choice: as positive / as negative / as a bit of both

b Why is it important? ✏ ....

c Does it link to other themes? ✏ ....

....

d Why does Priestley include the idea of guilt in the play? ✏ ....

....

....

....

2 **a** Note down ✏ **three** points to include in your response.

Point 1:

Point 2:

Point 3:

b Can you add key events as evidence for your points? Add ✏ notes to your points.

c Can your points be linked to the following? Add ✏ notes to your ideas above.

| setting | theme | structure | context | audience | characters |

Review your skills

Check up

Review your response to the exam-style question on page 39. Tick ✓ the column to show how well you think you have done each of the following.

	Not quite ✓	Nearly there ✓	Got it! ✓
used clear points that focus on the question	☐	☐	☐
linked the response to key themes and characters	☐	☐	☐
made a critical judgement	☐	☐	☐

Look over all of your work in this unit. Note down ✐ **three** points to remember when choosing a question on *An Inspector Calls*.

1. ....

2. ....

3. ....

Need more practice?

Try writing ✐ a response to the exam-style question below.

Exam-style question

Sheila: *You and I aren't the same people who sat down to dinner here.*

Explore the relationship between Sheila and Gerald.

You **must** refer to the context of the play in your answer.

(40 marks)

Spend some time unlocking the question before you begin your planning. After you have finished your writing, check your answer. Has it covered everything the question asks for?

How confident do you feel about each of these **skills?** Colour ✐ in the bars.

1. How do I choose a question?

2. How do I unlock the question?

3. How do I develop a critical judgement?

⑥ Planning your response

This unit will help you to plan your response to the exam question on *An Inspector Calls*. The skills you will build are to:

- support your critical judgement with relevant points
- use relevant evidence to support your points
- sequence your points to build a successful argument.

In the exam you will face questions like the ones below. At the end of the unit you will write your own response to one of these questions.

Exam-style question

Inspector: *It's my duty to ask questions.*

In what ways is the Inspector presented as powerful?

You **must** refer to the context of the play in your answer.   **(40 marks)**

Exam-style question

Sheila: *But these girls aren't cheap labour – they're people.*

Explore how ideas about inequality are important in the play.

You **must** refer to the context of the play in your answer.   **(40 marks)**

Before you tackle these questions, you will work through three key questions in the **skills boosts** to help you plan your response.

 ① **How do I make relevant points?**   **②** **How do I select relevant evidence?**   **③** **How do I sequence my points?**

Look at one student's plan on page 42 for the **second** exam-style above.

As you read the plan, think about whether the student has:

made relevant points that support the critical judgement	used relevant evidence that can be linked to context or audience response	sequenced the points effectively to build to a conclusion.
☐	☐	☐

Sheila: *But these girls aren't cheap labour – they're people.*

Explore how ideas about inequality are important in the play.

You **must** refer to the context of the play in your answer.

(40 marks)

Critical judgement – Priestley uses the play to comment on the lack of equality in society.

Inequality benefits the wealthy – easy lifestyle and power	• Stage directions at start – contrast between Edna clearing away dining room setting • Birlings in evening dress • Arthur boasts about expecting a knighthood
Eva used to represent effect of inequality on working classes – wealthy able to exploit	• Easily fired from jobs in factory and shop • Dependent on men – Gerald and Eric • Lack of opportunities shown by Arthur's question about whether Eva got into trouble (Act I) Shows inequality before welfare state and also the gender inequality of the time
Inspector challenges and suggests new way	• Argues with Arthur about Eva's sacking • Criticises factories that exploit working classes • Says 'We are responsible for each other' (Act III) Reflects Priestley's views about social responsibility – widely accepted today, but intended to educate original audience

Conclusion – Sheila and Eric represent hope for more equality in future

---

① The student has made points that support their critical judgement. Highlight and label ✐ the student's notes to show where the evidence they use to support their points will allow them to comment on '**context**' and '**audience response**'.

② How does the conclusion about Sheila and Eric link to the student's critical judgement? Write ✐ **one** or **two** sentences explaining the link.

....

....

....

How do I make relevant points?

You will need to make a range of points to support your critical judgement. It is important to focus on the words in the question, rather than just telling the story of the play or the characters.

Look again at one of the exam-style questions from page 40.

Exam-style question

In what ways is the Inspector presented as powerful?

(1) Your points should address the phrase 'in what ways' in the question. Look at some points about the presentation of the Inspector:

Presentation of the Inspector	✓	✗
He is not intimidated by the Birlings.		
He represents Priestley's ideas about responsibility.		
He challenges the Birlings and Gerald.		
He isn't a real Inspector.		
His visit turns out to be a hoax.		
Edna shows him in.		
He exposes the family's lack of morals.		

a Tick ✓ the four most relevant points.

b Put a cross ✗ next to the points you think are just telling the story.

(2) For a theme-based question, you should always consider the different ideas about the themes in the play.

Exam-style question

Explore how ideas about inequality are important in the play.

Look at one student's points about inequality.

Eva's life is difficult.	☐

Inequality allows wealthy to exploit working class.	☐

The Birlings are wealthy.	☐

Gerald is superior to the Birlings.	☐

Working class have fewer opportunities.	☐

The Birlings benefit from inequality.	☐

Which points cover 'ideas about inequality'? Tick ✓ them, then cross ✗ any ideas that simply tell the story of the play or characters.

② How do I select relevant evidence?

You will need to support each of your points with relevant evidence. Evidence should be a specific event from *An Inspector Calls* rather than a general statement, and you should cover the whole of the play. Evidence should also allow you to make links to context and audience response.

Look again at the **first** exam-style question on page 41. Then look at **points 1**, **2** and **3** below about how the Inspector is powerful.

Exam-style question

Inspector: *It's my duty to ask questions.*
In what ways is the Inspector presented as powerful?
You **must** refer to the context of the play in your answer.   **(40 marks)**

Point	Relevant evidence	Context or audience response
Point 1: He exposes the Birlings' lack of compassion for others.		
Point 2: He is not intimidated by the Birlings' superior class.		
Point 3: His power shows the importance of his message about responsibility.		

①   **a**   Now look at some of the Inspector's key moments from the play. Note ✏ the most relevant as evidence for each of the points above.

Act I A	He arrives as Arthur is talking about men being responsible for themselves.
Act I B	Soon after arriving, he interrupts Arthur.
Act I C	He refuses to let Gerald and Eric look at the photograph.
Act III D	He gives a final warning that if people don't take responsibility for others they will pay with 'fire and blood and anguish'.
Act II E	Mrs Birling refuses to take any blame for turning Eva away.
Act I F	He insists Gerald stays and listens to the questioning of Arthur.

b   For **one** of the points, write ✏ a sentence explaining why the evidence you have chosen supports the point.

....

....

②   Think about how your evidence could be used to comment on **context** or **audience response**. Write ✏ **C** or **AR** next to points 1 to 3 above to show where a relevant comment could be made. Then select **two** of the points and write ✏ **one** or **two** sentences explaining the link.

Point number ....

....

Point number ....

....

③ How do I sequence my points?

You need to sequence your points to build a logical argument that supports your critical judgement. The easiest way to do this is to take a chronological approach. However, you can also link your points by character, theme or author's approach.

Look at this exam-style question and one student's critical judgement in response to it.

Exam-style question

Explore how ideas about inequality are important in the play.

Priestley uses An Inspector Calls to explore his ideas about inequality in society.

Now look at these four key points, taken from the same student's plan.

A ☐ *Inequality shown through Eva's lack of opportunities.*

B ☐ *Inequality benefits wealthy like the Birlings and Gerald.*

C ☐ *Gender inequality shown through the way men use Eva.*

D ☐ *Inspector points out how society could be more equal.*

① One way to sequence the key points in a response is to work your way through the play **chronologically**: exploring how a character or theme develops as the play progresses. How would you sequence key points (**A–D**) above if you were organising a response **chronologically**? Number 🖉 the points in the boxes above.

chronological: in time order

② Another way to organise key points in a response is to **synthesise** them: grouping related points together – for example, about a character or the author's approach.

synthesise: combining or grouping

ⓐ Write 🖉 **one** sentence about how you would sequence key points **A–D** above if you were exploring how Priestley shows inequality first through one character, then through another.

....

....

ⓑ Write 🖉 **one** sentence about how you would sequence key points **A–D** above if you were looking at one way in which Priestley explores inequality, then another way in which he explores inequality, and so on.

....

....

③ ⓐ Tick ✓ the method **you** would choose to sequence key points **A–D** above.

☐ Chronologically

☐ Synthesising key points about character

☐ Synthesising key points about the author's approach

ⓑ On paper, write 🖉 **one** or **two** sentences explaining your choice.

Unit 6 Planning your response 45

Planning your response

To plan an effective response you need to:

- make relevant points that support your critical judgement
- support each of your points with relevant evidence that can be linked to context and audience response
- sequence your points – decide on the most effective way to build a logical argument that supports your critical judgement (for example, chronologically, by character or by approach).

Look again at the **first** exam-style question you saw at the start of the unit.

Exam-style question

Inspector: *It's my duty to ask questions.*

In what ways is the Inspector presented as powerful?

You **must** refer to the context of the play in your answer. **(40 marks)**

Look at these two paragraphs, written by a student in response to the exam-style question above.

> The Inspector is presented as powerful as he is used by Priestley to present his ideas about the need for an equal and just society.
>
> Priestley first suggests he is powerful as the stage directions describe him as creating an impression of 'massiveness' and as looking hard at the people he addresses before speaking. This suggests he will be an imposing and dominating figure who will achieve his aims. The lighting changes when he arrives, becoming brighter and harder, which symbolises his power and the fact that he will reveal the family's secrets. This would encourage an audience to see the Inspector as an important character and to listen carefully to what he has to say.
>
> In Act I he appears powerful as he refuses to be intimidated by the Birlings' superior social status. He is not impressed by Arthur's claims to know the local police. He interrupts him and also insists Gerald stays during the questioning of Arthur, despite Arthur's boasting that Gerald is from the upper classes. This powerful approach from a policeman might have surprised an audience in 1945, as wealthy families were used to commanding respect at that time. However, a modern audience would think it right that wealth does not put you above the law.

1. Underline Ⓐ where the student has supported their two points about the Inspector with relevant and specific evidence. Label 🖉 it '**evidence**'.

2. Highlight 🖉 where the student has made links to context and audience response. Label 🖉 them '**context**' or '**audience response**'.

3. Tick ✓ how this student has organised their key points.

   A chronologically ⬚   B by character ⬚   C by approach ⬚

Your turn!

You are now going to **write your own response** to the exam-style question below.

Exam-style question

Inspector: *It's my duty to ask questions.*

In what ways is the Inspector presented as powerful?

You **must** refer to the context of the play in your answer.   **(40 marks)**

(1) Note ✐ below the key points you will make in your response. Remember to consider the words in the question and make a range of points that cover the whole play.

Point 1:

Point 2:

Point 3:

Point 4:

(2) Which specific **events** or **speeches** in the play will you use as evidence for your points? Add them ✐ to your plan above.

(3) Which of your points can be linked to the ideas below? Note ✐ this on your plan.

context   audience response

(4) (a) How will you sequence your key points? Tick ✓ **one** answer.

☐ chronologically   ☐ by character   ☐ by approach

(b) Note ✐ the order of your key points so that you sequence them to build an argument that supports your critical judgement.

The order of my key points will be: ....

(5) Now write ✐ your response to the exam-style question above on paper.

Review your skills

Check up

Review your response to the exam-style question on page 47. Tick ✓ the column to show how well you think you have done each of the following.

	Not quite ✓	Nearly there ✓	Got it! ✓
made key points using key words from the question	☐	☐	☐
used relevant evidence that can be linked to structure, context and audience	☐	☐	☐
sequenced my key points to build an argument that supports my critical judgement	☐	☐	☐

Look over all of your work in this unit. Note down ✏ **three** points to remember when planning a response.

1. ....

2. ....

3. ....

Need more practice?

Try writing ✏ a response to the exam-style question below.

Exam-style question

Sheila: *But these girls aren't cheap labour – they're people.*

Explore how ideas about inequality are important in the play.

You **must** refer to the context of the play in your answer.

(40 marks)

Remember to start by underlining Ⓐ key words in the question.

How confident do you feel about each of these **skills?** Colour ✏ in the bars.

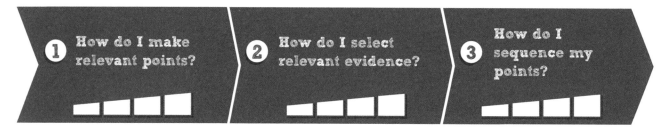

1. How do I make relevant points?
2. How do I select relevant evidence?
3. How do I sequence my points?

7 Using evidence

This unit will help you to use evidence effectively in your responses. The skills you will build are to:

- make references to the play to support your points
- make effective interpretations of the play's characters and themes
- structure your response to make your interpretations clear.

In the exam, you will face questions like the ones below. At the end of the unit you will write your own response to one of these questions.

Exam-style question

Mrs Birling: (agitated) *I don't believe it. I won't believe it …*

Explore the significance of the relationship between parents and children.

You **must** refer to the context of the play in your answer.   **(40 marks)**

Exam-style question

Sheila: *You don't seem to have learnt anything.*

Explore how learning from experience is important in the play.

You **must** refer to the context of the play in your answer.   **(40 marks)**

Before you tackle these questions, you will work through three key questions in the **skills boosts** to help you plan your response.

1 How do I make specific references to the play?

2 How do I interpret my evidence?

3 How do I structure my interpretations?

Look at the extract from one student's response on page 50 to the **second** question above.

As you read the extract, think about whether the student has:

made specific references to the play to support the points made	interpreted the evidence that has been used	linked the interpretation to key words in the question.

Sheila: *You don't seem to have learnt anything.*

Explore how learning from experience is important in the play.

You **must** refer to the context of the play in your answer. (40 marks)

At the start of the play, before the Inspector arrives, Arthur Birling presents himself as the voice of experience. For example, this is shown when he talks of having learned from his business experiences and when he boasts of his impending knighthood. This all suggests that he feels his experience is valuable enough to be listened to and rewarded.

Arthur Birling is also presented as very self-interested. This is clear when he talks to Gerald and Eric before the Inspector arrives, when he dismisses the ideas of community and lectures them about the need for men to look after themselves rather than others. This suggests he is not going to be very open to new ideas and has very little interest in things outside of his family and business.

① Underline (A) and label (✐) where the student has:
- used specific references to the play as evidence – label as 'SR'
- interpreted the evidence – label as '**interpretation**'
- linked interpretations to key words in the question – label as '**links**'.

② At what other specific points in the play does Priestley suggest that Arthur Birling does not learn from experience? Write down (✐) **two** key events.

Key event 1: ....

....

Key event 2: ....

....

1 How do I make specific references to the play?

When using evidence to support your points, you should use specific examples of events or speeches from the play rather than retelling the plot or relying on general comments about a character.

(1) Look at this point from a student's response to the **second** question on page 49.

Exam-style question

Explore how learning from experience is important in the play.

> Priestley presents Sheila as learning the most in the play.

Now look at some evidence that could be used to support the points.

> A Sheila starts the play as a rather shallow young girl, then she feels sorry for getting Eva sacked, then she criticises her parents, but at the end she recognises that the whole family is to blame.

> B For example, even after the Inspector's visit is shown to be a hoax she insists on remembering his warning speech that men will pay in the future if they do not learn their lesson.

> C She changes throughout the play and learns about equality for the working classes and about being responsible for other people.

(a) Which evidence refers to specific events and speeches in the play? Tick ✓ your choice.

(b) Which evidence relies too much on retelling the plot? Label it ✎ 'plot'.

(c) Which evidence is just a general comment? Label it ✎ 'general'.

(d) Look at your choice for part (a). Underline Ⓐ the words that show the evidence is specific and not general.

(2) Look at another point, this time from a student's response to the **first** question on page 49.

Exam-style question

Explore the significance of the relationship between parents and children.

> Priestley uses the relationship between parents and children to show how out of touch the older generation are.

Act I, when Eric is slightly drunk and Arthur is giving long speeches

Act II, at the end just before Eric comes back in

Act III, after the Inspector has gone

(a) Which points in the play above best support this point? Tick ✓ your choice.

(b) Which specific event or speech from that part of the play could be used as evidence? On paper, ✎ write **one** or **two** sentences explaining your choice.

2 How do I interpret my evidence?

When interpreting your evidence, it is important not to focus on the individual words and phrases used by Priestley. Interpretation means focusing on what the evidence suggests about characters and themes.

① Look at a point with supporting evidence from one student's response to the **second** question on page 49.

Exam-style question

Explore the significance of the relationship between parents and children.

> Priestley shows that the older generation are not able to learn from experience. This is shown when Arthur Birling finds out the Inspector was a hoax and starts to relax, offering Gerald a drink and imitating the Inspector.

Now look at several student attempts to interpret this evidence. Draw lines 🖉 to match each student attempt to the correct comment.

A This suggests that Arthur is able to dismiss the events of the evening easily and therefore that nothing the Inspector has said will leave a lasting impression on him.

a This just uses different words to repeat the evidence.

B This shows Arthur has not learned anything from his experience with the Inspector.

b This is interpretation, as it links the evidence to what it suggests about a character.

C This suggests Arthur is relieved about the hoax and is now able to laugh about it.

c This is just a general comment that repeats the point.

② Look at this point with supporting evidence in response to the **first** question on page 49.

> The relationship between Sheila and her mother is presented as very traditional at the start of the play. For example, her mother tells her off for teasing Gerald and explains to her that men have important work that means wives often have to accept second place to men's business interests.

ⓐ What does this suggest about the relationship between Sheila and her mother? Does Sybil treat Sheila as someone old enough to be married? Why does she feel able to tell her what to do? Write 🖉 **one** or **two** sentences of interpretation.

....

....

ⓑ Now look at the student's interpretation below in response to evidence about the relationship between Eric and his father. Complete it by circling Ⓐ the best word to introduce your interpretation, then write 🖉 the rest of the sentence. You can add a second sentence if you need to.

Traditional family roles begin to be challenged when the Inspector arrives. For example, Eric appears to criticise Arthur's decision to sack Eva when he questions why girls like Eva shouldn't be allowed to try for higher wages. This suggests/shows/would suggest/hints to the audience ....

....

....

③ How do I structure my interpretations?

To make it clear that you are making interpretations, it is important that you structure your points carefully. You can use a Point – Evidence – Interpretation structure.

Point	Specific evidence	Interpretation
The older generation are shown to be self-centred.	This is shown immediately after the Inspector has left when all Arthur Birling can think about is the potential public scandal that will ensue if the news about Eva gets out.	This suggests that he has learned nothing as his immediate concern is not for Eva but for himself and his reputation.
↑ Clear point	↑ Evidence from a specific part of the play, referring to a specific event or speech: This is clear when … This is shown when … For example … For instance …	↑ Interpretation that links evidence to character or theme: This suggests … This makes it clear that … This shows … At this point the audience would realise …
↓ The younger generation are shown to be capable of learning from experience.	↓ This is clear at the end of the play when Sheila refuses to take back Gerald's ring, as she needs to think.	↓ This shows the audience that she has changed and is no longer the shallow girl who was easily excited by an engagement ring.

① ⓐ Complete ✎ the table below with specific evidence and interpretations in response to the **first** question on page 49.

Exam-style question

Explore the significance of the relationship between parents and children.

Point	Specific evidence	Interpretation
Priestley shows that the older generation find it difficult to understand their children.		
Later in the play, the children are shown to be more responsible than the parents.		

ⓑ Look again at your evidence. Circle Ⓐ the best description of it: **specific / general**

ⓒ Look again at your interpretations. Tick ✓ the best description of them.

☐ They explain a link between the evidence and character or theme.

☐ They have just re-phrased the evidence.

ⓓ Re-write ✎ your responses if necessary on paper.

Using evidence

To use evidence effectively to support your points, you need to:
- use specific examples of events or speeches
- interpret your evidence by considering what it suggests about characters and themes
- structure your interpretation carefully.

Now look at the first exam-style question you saw at the start of the unit.

Exam-style question

Mrs Birling: (agitated) *I don't believe it. I won't believe it ...*

Explore the significance of the relationship between parents and children.

You **must** refer to the context of the play in your answer.

(40 marks)

Read this paragraph, taken from one student's response to this question.

Key features of an effective interpretation

At the end of the play the relationships between Eric and his father is badly damaged. This is shown when, soon after the Inspector has left, Eric openly challenges Arthur's authority by shouting at him that they all killed Eva and Arthur responds by threatening his son. This makes Arthur seems very aggressive and at this point the audience would realise that Arthur has learned nothing, as he is just as unpleasant as he was at the start of the play.

The relationship between Sheila and her parents is also broken by the end of the play. This is made very clear after the Inspector has gone, when she responds to her father's mockery about the Inspector and the death of Eva by moving towards the door. This suggests she wants nothing more to do with her parents and wishes to distance herself from their views.

> key point focusing on the key words in the question

> specific events or speeches used as evidence

> interpretations that are linked to character or theme

> phrases used to structure the interpretation (for this example, 'This suggests ...')

---

(1) Can you identify all the different things the student has included in this paragraph? Use lines and circles (A) to link each annotation to part of the student's answer.

Your turn!

You are now going to **write your own response** to the exam-style question below.

Exam-style question

Mrs Birling: (agitated) *I don't believe it. I won't believe it …*

Explore the significance of the relationship between parents and children.

You **must** refer to the context of the play in your answer. (40 marks)

(1) How do you think Priestley uses the relationship between parents and children? What ideas does he explore? Write (✐) **one** sentence giving your critical judgement in response to the question.

....

....

(2) List below (✐) the key points you will make in your response. Remember to consider the words in the question and make a range of points that cover the whole play.

Point 1:

Point 2:

Point 3:

Point 4:

(3) Now add (✐) evidence to each of your points. Remember to:
- avoid telling the story
- avoid general statements
- use specific events or speeches.

(4) How will you interpret your evidence? Make notes (✐) above and remember to:
- avoid rephrasing the evidence
- think about what the evidence suggests about the character.

(5) You will also need to make links to the context of the play for at least one of your points. Add (✐) a relevant contextual idea to one of your points.

(6) Now write (✐) your response on paper.

Review your skills

Check up

Review your response to the exam-style question on page 55. Tick ✓ the column to show how well you think you have done on each of the following.

	Not quite ✓	Nearly there ✓	Got it! ✓
used specific events or speeches as evidence	☐	☐	☐
interpreted the evidence	☐	☐	☐
structured my interpretations	☐	☐	☐

Look over all of your work in this unit. Note down 🖉 **three** points to remember when planning a response.

1. ....

2. ....

3. ....

Need more practice?

Try writing 🖉 a response to the exam style question below.

Exam-style question

Sheila: *You don't seem to have learnt anything.*

Explore how learning from experience is important in the play.

You **must** refer to the context of the play in your answer. (40 marks)

Think about:

• how Priestley uses language to show character

• specific types of language or language features used

• connotations of individual words or phrases.

How confident do you feel about each of these **skills?** Colour 🖉 in the bars.

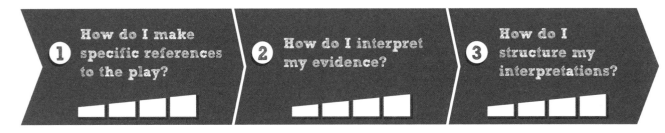

1. How do I make specific references to the play?

2. How do I interpret my evidence?

3. How do I structure my interpretations?

⑧ Writing a response

This unit will help you to develop your points in your response. The skills you will build are to:

- link interpretations to context and audience
- develop your points with extra evidence
- extend your interpretations.

In the exam you will face questions like the ones below. At the end of this unit you will write your own response to one of these questions.

Exam-style question

Inspector: *Just used her … as if she was an animal, a thing, not a person.*

In what ways is Eva Smith exploited in the play?

You **must** refer to the context of the play in your answer.   (40 marks)

Exam-style question

Arthur: *But you youngsters just remember what I said.*

Explore the importance of age in *An Inspector Calls*.

You **must** refer to the context of the play in your answer.   (40 marks)

Before you tackle these questions, you will work through three key questions in the **skills boosts** to help you write your response.

① How do I develop my evidence? **② How do I develop my interpretations?** **③ How do I link my interpretations to context?**

Look at two paragraphs from one student's response on page 58 to the **first** question above.

As you read the paragraphs, think about: ✓

how the student has used evidence ☐

how the student has developed each point ☐

how the student has linked interpretation to contextual ideas. ☐

Exam-style question

Inspector: *Just used her ... as if she was an animal, a thing, not a person.*

In what ways is Eva Smith exploited in the play?

You **must** refer to the context of the play in your answer.

(40 marks)

Eva Smith is used by Priestley to represent the working classes and show how easily they were exploited by the wealthy. For example, she is not seen on stage, she is only described by others. This is important as it shows how wealthy families like the Birlings rely on the working classes without ever really seeing them as real people. This reflects the gap between the upper and lower classes in Edwardian society.

| link between interpretation and context |

| a point that links to the question |

| interpretation |

| evidence about how a character is presented |

Eva Smith is first presented to the audience through Arthur Birling in a positive way. This is shown when Arthur praises her, calling her good looking and a good worker. This suggests he thought she was a good employee. This was not unusual, as many factories liked employing women in 1912 because women could be paid less than men and were not under the protection of trade unions. This meant that if the women protested about their low pay, they could easily be sacked. This is shown in the play when Arthur defends his sacking of Eva, saying she had to go as she had 'too much to say'. Gerald immediately agrees with Arthur, which suggests that this lack of concern for the rights of the working classes was common at the time.

| extra evidence |

| a clear point |

| interpretation |

| link between interpretation and context |

| how context is shown in play |

| evidence |

| interpretation of extra evidence |

---

1 Read both paragraphs above. Then draw a line 🖉 linking each comment to the relevant part of its paragraph. Underline Ⓐ all the words in the paragraph that apply to each comment.

1 How do I develop my evidence?

A good response will develop each point in detail. One way to do this is to add further evidence to support your points.

A developed response will use more than one piece of evidence to support each point. For example:

> **Priestley initially presents Sheila as a rather naïve young woman.**
>
> This is first <u>apparent when she accepts without question Gerald's excuses about his absences during the previous summer</u> and it then becomes more obvious <u>when she assumes it was an accident that Eva Smith drank the disinfectant.</u> This suggests her youthful naivety as she cannot imagine anyone being capable of taking their own life.

Two different pieces of evidence used to support the point.

Interpretation

(1) Consider this point:

> When the Inspector arrives, the younger generation start to challenge traditional age roles.

Evidence	Interpretation
This is first shown when Eric criticises his father for sacking Eva. It is then shown when	This suggests ....

a Add ✎ evidence to the table to develop the response.

b Comment ✎ on the effect of the evidence in the 'interpretation' column.

(2) Look again at the **first** exam-style question from page 57.

Exam-style question

In what ways is Eva Smith exploited in the play?

Point: Sybil Birling also abuses her power over Eva.	
Evidence	Interpretation
This is shown when	This suggests ....
This is also seen when	

Point: Eric exploits Eva sexually.	
Evidence	Interpretation
For example	This suggests ....
This is also seen when	

a Add ✎ **two** pieces of developed evidence to each of the points above about Eva's exploitation.

b Add ✎ your interpretation of the evidence.

2 How do I develop my interpretations?

Another way to develop your points is to think about additional interpretations, which can be linked to either character or theme.

(1) Look again at the question about Eva's exploitation. Then read and complete ✎ one student's notes.

Think about what 'disinfectant' might symbolise in the play. What is it used for?

Exam-style question

Inspector: *Just used her … as if she was an animal, a thing, not a person.*

In what ways is Eva Smith exploited in the play?

You **must** refer to the context of the play in your answer.   (40 marks)

Point 1	Evidence	Interpretation	Additional interpretation
Arthur is presented as exploiting Eva for cheap labour.	This is shown when he justifies his sacking of her by saying it is his duty to keep labour costs down.	This suggests he sees the workers as raw materials for his business, rather than as people.	It also shows he has no sense of social responsibility as he feels his main duty is to make a profit, not to look after people outside of his family.

Point 2			
Eva's death is used to show how damaging exploitation could be.	For example, the Inspector refers to her having killed herself by swallowing a lot of strong disinfectant.	This creates a horrible image and suggests Eva must have been really desperate.	It also

(2) Use the space below ✎ to make additional interpretations for both of the points above. If your first interpretations were linked to character, try to develop your point by linking to a theme.

3 How do I link my interpretations to context?

When writing about context or audience response it is important that your comments flow smoothly from your interpretations, rather than standing alone as general comments.

(1) Look at this paragraph from one student's response to the question about Eva's exploitation.

Exam-style question

In what ways is Eva Smith exploited in the play?

> Sheila is also shown as capable of exploiting Eva, through her social status. This is shown by her petty jealousy over Eva who she causes to be sacked just because she thought Eva was mocking her. This suggests Sheila felt superior to Eva, and felt justified in using her power to get her dismissed.

A This reflects the fact that it would have been easy for a girl like Eva to be sacked in 1912 as there was little employment protection and very few trade unions.

B A modern audience would not agree with Sheila's treatment of Eva.

C In 1912, unmarried working class girls would have struggled without a job as there was no unemployment benefit.

Which sentence best completes the student's paragraph? Circle Ⓐ A, B or C.

(2) Read another student's **point-evidence-interpretation** paragraph. The student could complete it by commenting on context or on the response of an audience in 1945 or today. Complete ✎ their comments below.

> **Point:** Gerald and Eric are both shown to have abused their power over Eva.
>
> **Evidence:** For example, Gerald took her as his mistress as he felt sorry for her and says he was protecting her from the unwelcome advances of men like Alderman Meggarty.
>
> **Interpretation:** This suggests that he felt justified in taking advantage of Eva's desperation. It also suggests he felt some guilt over his treatment of her, as he tries to find excuses for his behaviour.
>
> Contextual comment: ....
>
> ....
>
> ....
>
> ....
>
> Audience comment: ....
>
> ....
>
> ....
>
> ....

Writing a response

To write an effective response you need to:

- develop your evidence
- make additional interpretations
- make smooth links between your interpretations and your contextual ideas.

Look again at the **second** exam-style question you saw at the start of the unit.

Exam-style question

Arthur: *But you youngsters just remember what I said.*

Explore the importance of age in *An Inspector Calls*.

You **must** refer to the context of the play in your answer. (40 marks)

Read this paragraph, taken from one student's response to this question.

> Traditional ideas about age are presented at the start of the play. For instance, Sheila is presented as rather childish as she still refers to her parents as 'Mummy' and 'Daddy' despite being engaged to Gerald. She is also still treated as a child by her mother, who answers for her when she doesn't reply to Gerald's question about being part of the family. This shows that her mother expects Sheila to do what she is told. It also suggests that Sybil is concerned about impressing Gerald as he is considered to be a good catch for Sheila. This reflects the traditional view that young people should respect and obey their elders, and this would have been even more expected at the time the play was set.
>
> Eric is also presented as rather childish at the start of the play. For example, he suddenly laughs for no reason and appears to be drunk. His behaviour is obviously unacceptable to the Birling parents as they look at him and even Sheila talks to him 'severely'. This suggests he is an irresponsible character as he offers no reason for his inappropriate behaviour. It also hints that he might be an unpredictable character later in the play.
>
> Later in the play Eric begins to challenge his parents more openly …

1 **a** Underline Ⓐ where the student has used more than one piece of evidence to support a point. Label ✎ this '**evidence**'.

b Circle Ⓐ where the student has developed their response with additional interpretations. Label ✎ as '**AI**'.

c Highlight ✎ where the student has used context that flows clearly from the point. Label ✎ as '**Flows clearly**'.

2 What evidence would you use for the final point about Eric? On paper, try to write ✎ **one or more** pieces of evidence to fully support the point.

Your turn!

You are now going to **write a response** to the exam-style question below.

Exam-style question

Inspector: *Just used her ... as if she was an animal, a thing, not a person.*

In what ways is Eva Smith exploited in the play?

You **must** refer to the context of the play in your answer. **(40 marks)**

(1) How do you think Priestley presents Eva Smith? What ideas about exploitation does he explore? Write ✐ **one** sentence giving your critical judgement in response to the question.

....

....

(2) Note below ✐ the key points you will make in your response.

Remember to consider the words in the question and make a range of points that cover the whole play.

Point 1:

Point 2:

Point 3:

Point 4:

(3) Add ✐ evidence and links to contextual ideas and audience responses to support your points.

(4) Look carefully at your plan. Is there anywhere you could develop your points by adding ✐ more evidence or additional interpretations?

(5) Now write ✐ your response on paper.

Review your skills

Review your response to the exam-style question on page 63. Tick ✓ the column to show how well you think you have done on each of the following.

	Not quite ✓	Nearly there ✓	Got it! ✓
developed my evidence	☐	☐	☐
made additional interpretations	☐	☐	☐
linked contextual or audience ideas smoothly	☐	☐	☐

Look over all of your work in this unit. Note down ✏ **three** points to remember when writing a response.

1. ....

2. ....

3. ....

Need more practice?

Try writing ✏ a response to the exam style question below.

Exam-style question

Arthur: *But you youngsters just remember what I said.*

Explore the importance of age in *An Inspector Calls*.

You **must** refer to the context of the play in your answer.   (40 marks)

Remember to start your response with a
critical judgment that sums up your ideas.

How confident do you feel about each of these **skills?** Colour ✏ in the bars.

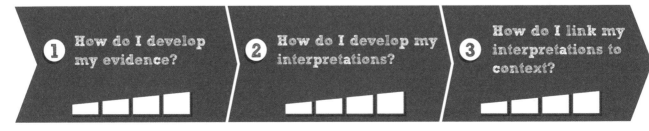

1 How do I develop my evidence?

2 How do I develop my interpretations?

3 How do I link my interpretations to context?

⑨ Developing a critical writing style

This unit will help you to express your ideas about *An Inspector Calls* as clearly and precisely as possible. The skills you will build are to:

- select vocabulary to expand your ideas and express them precisely
- link your ideas to express them clearly
- extend your sentences to develop your ideas more fully.

In the exam you will face questions like the ones below. At the end of the unit you will write a paragraph in response to one of these questions.

Exam-style question

Gerald: *Everything's all right now, Sheila.* [Holds up the ring]

Explore the importance of love in *An Inspector Calls*.

You **must** refer to the context of the play in your answer.   (40 marks)

Exam-style question

Inspector: *Apologise for what? Doing my duty?*

In what ways is the Inspector important in the play?

You **must** refer to the context of the play in your answer.   (40 marks)

Before you tackle these questions, you will work through three key questions in the **skills boosts** to help you plan your response.

① How do I choose precise vocabulary?

② How do I link my ideas to express them more clearly?

③ How do I extend my sentences to develop my ideas more fully?

Look at an extract from one student's response on page 66 to the **first** exam-style question above.

As you read the extract, think about whether the student has:

used a range of ambitious and precise vocabulary ☐

linked sentences so that ideas are expressed clearly ☐

used a range of sentence styles to develop ideas fully. ☐

Gerald: *Everything's all right now, Sheila.* [Holds up the ring]

Explore the importance of love in *An Inspector Calls*.

> Priestley uses the theme of love in *An Inspector Calls* to explore ideas about the different values of men and women.
>
> When the play opens, love is presented in a positive way. For example, the family are celebrating Sheila and Gerald's engagement and are pleased with themselves. Also, during the toast to the couple, Sheila and Gerald look at each other. At this time Sheila is quiet and serious. This suggests they are deeply committed to each other while also reflecting a romantic view of love that audiences would find easy to relate to and understand.
>
> However, there are suggestions of unease about the relationship in Sheila's behaviour. For example, her first speech is directed to be spoken 'gaily'. It is also supposed to be said 'possessively'. This has connotations of a clingy and demanding character. This jealous side to her character is also hinted at by her reaction to the ring as she says she now feels really engaged, which encourages an audience to feel that she had some doubts about Gerald's commitment before that night.
>
> Gerald also shows signs of uncertainty. When he responds to the toast he says he hopes he will deserve Sheila, suggesting he has some qualms about the relationship. He also asks whether he is now part of the family and repeats himself when Sheila fails to answer. This might all suggest to an audience that both Gerald and Sheila have had some reservations about their relationship.

1 Circle Ⓐ **three** examples of ambitious vocabulary. Label 🖉 them '**ambitious**'.

2 Underline Ⓐ **three** examples of conjunctions used to link sentences. Label 🖉 them '**conjunctions**'.

3 Highlight 🖉 any sentences you feel could be linked to create a more critical style. Label 🖉 them '**critical style**'.

4 What other ideas about love are present in *An Inspector Calls*? List 🖉 **three**.

Idea 1: ....

Idea 2: ....

Idea 3: ....

1 How do I choose precise vocabulary?

You need to choose precise vocabulary in your responses to show full understanding of Priestley's main ideas. To do this, you should build up a bank of ambitious vocabulary for each of the key characters and themes.

1 These key points relate to ideas about love and relationships in *An Inspector Calls*. For each point, choose one word from the list below and write it below the relevant point. Use at least **one** word from each column.

Choose words that describe love *at that point in the play*. Aim to be as precise as possible.

Act I	Act II	Act III
Arthur Birling speaks about the engagement and his business hopes.	Gerald talks about saving Eva from Alderman Meggarty.	Eric says he insisted on going back to Eva's lodgings for sex.
Gerald defends his lack of attention to Sheila over the summer.	Gerald says Eva loved him and he was the most important person in her life.	Eric says he did not love Eva 'or anything'.
Sybil Birling warns Sheila that men will always put business first.	Sheila returns Gerald's engagement ring.	Gerald asks Sheila to take the ring back as 'Everything's all right now.'

romantic	unequal	hypocritical	damaging
arranged	unrealistic	dishonest	exploitative
faithfulness	fairy tale	sordid	squalid
commitment	contrasting	demanding	dangerous
contented	insincere	cruel	manipulative

2 Think about the Inspector at key points in the play. For each point, choose one word from the list below and write it below the relevant point.

Try to choose a different word each time so you show a full understanding of every aspect of the Inspector's character.

Act I	Act II	Act III
He tells the Birlings that Eva died 'after several hours of agony'.	Sheila warns her mother that the Inspector knows everything.	He warns the Birlings that everybody has a responsibility to care for each other.
He interrupts Arthur Birling's impatient protest: 'cutting through, massively'.	Sybil Birling says he has made a big impression on the younger generation.	His visit proves to be a hoax.

judgemental	powerful	symbolic	commanding
mysterious	omniscient	challenging	imposing
dominating	distinctive	moral	formidable
righteous	prophetic	dramatic	compassionate

② How do I link my ideas to express them more clearly?

You should use conjunctions to link your ideas, as this will help you to express those ideas more fluently.

Coordinating conjunctions link related or contrasting ideas:

| and | but | or | so |

Remember to choose and position your conjunction carefully to express each idea as clearly and fluently as possible.

Subordinating conjunctions express more complex connections:

- an explanation – for example: | because | in order to | as a result | consequently |

- a comparison – for example: | although | however | on the other hand | whereas |

- a sequence – for example: | when | after | until | first |

① Look at these pairs of sentences. Circle Ⓐ the conjunctions in the sentences labelled **B**.

> **A** Arthur Birling protests about the Inspector's visit. The Inspector interrupts him by 'cutting in'.

> **B** When Arthur Birling protests about his visit, the Inspector interrupts him by 'cutting in'.

> **A** Sheila realises early in the play that she is partly responsible for Eva's death. Arthur continues to feel that he was justified in treating Eva harshly.

> **B** Sheila realises early in the play that she is partly responsible for Eva's death, whereas Arthur continues to feel that he was justified in treating her harshly.

② Re-write ✐ the following pairs of sentences, using a conjunction to link them.

a The Inspector questions each of the family in turn. **+** He wants to build up a 'chain of events' that will make them consider their behaviour.

....

....

b The Inspector challenges Arthur over his treatment of Eva. **+** Arthur tries to justify his decision to dismiss her.

....

....

c Sheila believes in the idea of romantic love at the start of the play. **+** She is more realistic at the end when she refuses to take back Gerald's ring.

....

....

3 How do I extend my sentences to develop my ideas more fully?

One way to extend your sentences and develop your ideas is by using conjunctions. Other ways include using:

- present participles: a verb ending in -ing
- the pronoun which.

Conjunctions			
and	but	when	as
before	after	although	if
whereas	unless	because	since

Look at this sentence:

> Arthur boasts about having been Lord Mayor and an Alderman …

You could complete it in four ways, using:

- this conjunction → (as soon as) the Inspector arrives.

- a different conjunction → (in order to) appear important.

- a present participle → belie(ving) it will impress the Inspector.

- which → (which) just makes the Inspector impatient.

1 Complete ✎ this sentence in **four** different ways:

> Sybil Birling insists the Inspector do his duty …

a using a conjunction: ....

b using a different conjunction: ....

c using a present participle: ....

d using which: ....

2 Annotate ✎ this student's sentences to make them a single sentence. Use a present participle or which.

a The Inspector takes his duties very seriously. <u>This encourages</u> the audience to see him as having high moral standards.

b Sybil Birling is rude to the Inspector and says his comments are 'impertinent'. <u>This creates</u> the impression that she is arrogant.

3 Re-read all the sentences you have written on this page to check that they are fluently and clearly expressed. Re-write ✎ any that are not.

....

....

....

....

....

....

....

You can use which or a present participle to avoid starting sentences with 'This suggests …' or 'This shows …'. For example:

- Gerald was engaged to Sheila when he had an affair with Eva which suggests he had double standards.
- Gerald was engaged to Sheila when he had an affair with Eva, suggesting he had double standards.

Developing a critical writing style

To express your ideas clearly and precisely, you need to:
- select ambitious vocabulary that expresses your ideas precisely
- use conjunctions, present participles and *which* to link your ideas and express them clearly.

Look again at the **second** exam-style question you saw at the start of the unit.

> **Exam-style question**
>
> **Inspector:** *Apologise for what? Doing my duty?*
>
> In what ways is the Inspector important in the play?
>
> You **must** refer to the context of the play in your answer. (40 marks)

Look at this short paragraph from one student's response to the question.

> At the start of the play the Inspector is presented as a good character. He is described in the stage directions as giving an impression of 'massiveness'. He is not bothered by Arthur Birling's boasting about being Mayor. Arthur gets impatient with him. Gerald gets annoyed. The Inspector stays cool and speaks 'gravely'. He also interrupts Arthur. He makes Arthur tell him what he did to Eva. This suggests the Inspector is going to be a big character in the play.

1 **a** Underline (A) at least **three** examples of vocabulary that could be more precise.

   b Note down in the margin at least **three** alternative vocabulary choices for each one.

   c Highlight any sentences you feel should be linked or developed to improve the clarity and precision of the writing.

   d Write an improved version of this paragraph, either by adjusting the text above or by re-writing it in the space below.

Your turn!

You are now going to **write one paragraph** in response to the exam-style question below.

Exam-style question

Inspector: *Apologise for what? Doing my duty?*

In what ways is the Inspector important in the play?

You **must** refer to the context of the play in your answer. (40 marks)

1. In what ways is the Inspector important in the play?

   Idea 1: ....

   ....

   Idea 2: ....

   ....

   Idea 3: ....

   ....

   Idea 4: ....

   ....

2. Choose **one** of your ideas and expand with evidence and a link to a theme. Note down your ideas below.

3. Now add some ambitious vocabulary to your ideas. Remind yourself of these words to describe the Inspector.

judgemental	powerful	symbolic	commanding
mysterious	omniscient	challenging	imposing
dominating	distinctive	moral	formidable
righteous	prophetic	dramatic	compassionate

4. Use your ideas to write **one** paragraph in response to the exam-style question on paper. Remember to:
   - choose your vocabulary carefully
   - think about ways in which you can link your ideas to develop and express them clearly and precisely.

5. When you have finished, read your paragraph.

   a. Underline Ⓐ where you have used ambitious vocabulary.

   b. Circle Ⓐ where you have joined sentences effectively.

   c. Highlight where you have developed your sentences to make your writing more fluent.

Review your skills

Check up

Review your response to the exam-style question on page 71. Tick ✓ the column to show how well you think you have done each of the following.

	Not quite ✓	Nearly there ✓	Got it! ✓
used ambitious vocabulary	☐	☐	☐
used conjunctions, present participles and the pronoun *which* to link your ideas and express them clearly	☐	☐	☐

Look over all of your work in this unit. Note down ✎ **three** points to remember when trying to express your ideas as clearly and precisely as possible.

1. ....

2. ....

3. ....

Need more practice?

You can EITHER:

1. Look again at your paragraph written in response to the exam-style question on page 71. Re-write ✎ it, experimenting with different vocabulary choices and sentence structures, linking your ideas in different ways. Which paragraph is most effective in expressing your ideas clearly and precisely?

AND/OR:

2. Write ✎ **one** paragraph in response to the exam-style question below. Remember to focus on your vocabulary choices and your sentence structures.

Exam-style question

Gerald: *Everything's all right now, Sheila.* [Holds up the ring]

Explore the importance of love in *An Inspector Calls*.

You **must** refer to the context of the play in your answer. (40 marks)

How confident do you feel about each of these **skills?** Colour ✎ in the bars.

1 How do I choose precise vocabulary?

2 How do I link my ideas to express them more clearly?

3 How do I extend my sentences to develop my ideas more fully?

Answers

Unit 1

Page 2

(1) For example:

Key point 2: Mr Birling tries to dominate Eric and treats him like a child by telling him to keep quiet when he interrupts.

Key point 3: Early in Act I Sheila is more interested in her engagement ring than in serious conversation.

(2) For example, points 1, 4 and 5.

(3) For example: Sheila refuses to take part in a toast; this shows she is challenging her parents and it highlights the difference between the old and young people's responses to Eva.

Page 3

(1) **(a)** 1 – Arthur; 2 – Sheila; 3 – Gerald; 4 – Mrs B; 5 – Eric

(b) Eva Smith

(c) For example: A relaxed mood is created as the setting is a prosperous dining room, the characters are dressed for dinner and the lighting is 'pink and intimate'. The characters are all happy as they are celebrating Sheila's engagement and are 'pleased with themselves'.

(2) **(a)** For example, 'Just a knighthood, of course'.

(b) Mr Birling is boasting and the word 'just' suggests he hopes for even higher status in the future.

(3) **(a)**

Order of events	Events	Character responsible
3	Eva changes her name to Daisy Renton and starts a relationship with a man. She moves away when he breaks off the relationship.	Gerald
4	Eva meets a man in Brumley and gets pregnant. He steals money to support her.	Eric
2	Eva works at Milwards until she is sacked because of a complaint about her.	Sheila
5	Eva asks for help from the Brumley Women's Charity but is refused.	Mrs Birling
1	Eva organises a strike at Birling and Company and is sacked.	Arthur Birling

Page 4

(1) **(b)** For example: The Inspector revealing that Eva was pregnant raises the tension as the audience will start to connect her with Eric – as he is the only family member not to have been questioned and he is not on stage.

(2) **(a)** 1 = Eric and Mr Birling argue about the stolen money.

2 = Sheila questions whether Goole was really an Inspector.

3 = Mr Birling rings Chief Constable Roberts.

4 = Gerald rings the infirmary.

(b) For example: The audience would start to question whether the Inspector was real and would be feeling tension about how the characters will react to the hoax.

Page 5

(1) **(a)** A = c, B = a, C = b

(2) **(b)** For example: The fact that Eric challenges his father over the strike suggests that the traditional age relationships in the play are starting to change, and it is youth that is becoming responsible and mature.

(3) **(b)** For example: The fact that Eric shows distress and shame over his part in Eva's fate suggests that he has learned from experience and is becoming less immature.

Page 6

(1) The student has shown a clear focus on the question and shown an understanding of the plot/structure of the play by starting with how Eric is presented at the start and going through the stages of his change. The events selected are the most significant for the question and fully support the points being made.

Page 7

(1) 1 Eric is drunk at the celebratory party.

2 Mr Birling calls the *Titanic* 'unsinkable'.

3 Mr Birling is told Eva has killed herself using bleach.

4 Sheila tells her father not to interfere in her engagement.

5 Mrs Birling tells Sheila not to contradict her.

6 Mrs Birling insists the father of the unborn child is to blame.

7 Sheila accuses her parents of being childish by not facing facts.

8 Mr Birling relaxes when the Inspector has gone and pours drinks.

9 Eric agrees with Sheila that their parents' reaction is frightening.

10 Gerald tries to give back the engagement ring.

(2) 2 Mr Birling calls the *Titanic* 'unsinkable'.

3 Mr Birling is told Eva has killed herself using bleach.

8 Mr Birling relaxes when the Inspector has gone and pours drinks.

10 Gerald tries to give back the engagement ring.

(3) 7 Sheila accuses her parents of being childish by not facing facts – 'It's you two who are being childish – trying not to face the facts.'

9 Eric agrees with Sheila that their parents' reaction is frightening – 'And I agree with Sheila. It frightens me too.'

(4) 4   Sheila tells her father not to interfere in her engagement.

7   Sheila accuses her parents of being childish by not facing facts.

9   Eric agrees with Sheila that their parents' reaction is frightening.

Unit 2

Page 10

(1) For example: Arthur is shown as the most powerful character as he has the most lines, which suggests he is the most important.

(2) For example: When Arthur jokes about the events it shows he has not taken the Inspector's visit seriously and has learned nothing.

(3) Reputation

Page 11

(1) All the words are appropriate.

(2) All the words are appropriate.

(3) Mr Birling – arrogant; Eric – shocked; Sheila – sympathetic; Gerald – indifferent

Page 12

(1) **a** For example: Wishes she hadn't been told about Eva's death; Warns her mother that the Inspector knows everything; After Inspector goes, criticises parents for not changing

b For example: Sheila's initial reaction to the news about Eva is sympathy, but she soon wishes she hadn't been told. This suggests she is still immature at this point. However, by the end of the play she has learned to take responsibility for her actions and is shocked by her parents' behaviour.

(2) For example: no change – Arthur and Sybil; slight remorse – Gerald; some remorse – Eric; extreme remorse – Sheila

(3) For example: The Inspector appears mysterious when he shows the photograph and then takes it back as the audience will wonder why he can't show it to all the characters at the same time.

Page 13

(1) For example: Mr Birling – feels his only duty is to himself, his business and his family; Sybil – shows no sense of responsibility despite running a charity; Sheila – shows she has developed a sense of responsibility as she is able to admit her part in Eva's fate by having her turned out of a job.

(2) **a** 'Between us we drove that girl to commit suicide'

b For example: Sheila has developed a sense of social responsibility as she recognises that her family's actions caused Eva's death.

(3) For example: Arthur tells Sybil to thank 'cook' – equality; Arthur expresses regret that Gerald's parents can't be at the party – love; Arthur worries that he will lose his chance of a knighthood – reputation.

Page 14

(1) **a** For example: 'at the start of the play as typical of the wealthy middle class', 'initially presented as rather shallow', 'described mainly in terms of her appearance', etc.

b For example: 'she begins to challenge her father', 'her emerging sense of responsibility'.

c For example: 'wealthy middle class', 'her emerging sense of responsibility'.

(2) For example: age and equality could be annotated.

Unit 3

Page 18

(1) 'He says: 'We don't live alone. We are members of one body. We are responsible for each other.' (Act I)'

(2) For example: 'Mr and Mrs Birling don't change'; 'Sheila and Eric start to take responsibility'

Page 19

(1) **b** For example: c ('Mrs Birling turns Eva away from her charity') can be linked to **B** (morality) because Mrs Birling makes herself morally superior by judging Eva.

(2) **b** For example:

Power: When Arthur says 'a man has to make his own way' he is showing the determination and strength to succeed.

Morality: When Arthur says 'you'd think everybody has to look after everybody else … community and all that nonsense' he is showing that he is really only interested in looking after himself.

Page 20

(1) **a** For example: as belonging to the middle classes, negative, dangerous, corrupting and taken for granted.

b For example: When Arthur Birling tells the Inspector that he used to be Lord Mayor he is using his power to try to influence things. This shows power can be corrupting.

(2) **a** Key event 1 is most relevant as evidence for Statement 1.

b For example: At this point in the play I think Priestley wants the audience to think that the younger generation are more in touch with modern thinking than the older generation, which gives them greater power in this situation.

(3) At the start, power is shown to belong to the middle classes when Arthur boasts about his impending knighthood. However, later in the play, the power shifts from the middle class Birlings to the Inspector and this is shown when he is described as 'taking charge masterfully'.

Page 21

(1) For example:

Responsibility = Inspector. In Act III he tells Mrs Birling he will make sure the father of Eva's child is held responsible.

Equality = Eva. In Act I she was unable to fight for a better standard of living as she could not manage with no wages while on strike.

(2) (a) They are all appropriate – except, perhaps, responsibility.

(b) For example: Equality – 'EDNA, the parlourmaid, is just clearing the table'

(3) For example: Stage 1 – Sheila abused her responsibility as a wealthy middle class woman to get Eva dismissed for no reason.

Page 22

(1) Key events – for example, Arthur calling people 'cranks'.

(2) For example, 'At the start of the play, Priestley suggests that the wealthy middle class has no sense of responsibility for others. This is shown through the Birlings, who are presented as wealthy by the comfortable setting'

(3) For example: In contrast, the Inspector is used to promote the idea of responsibility as he forces the other characters in turn to face up to their part in Eva's death.

Unit 4

Page 26

(1) For example: 'represents division of classes at the time'

(2) For example: Priestley was saying the division of the classes was wrong – Arthur Birling says the working classes should be treated harshly, but he also describes the *Titanic* as 'unsinkable' which implies his views are wrong.

(3) For example: Modern audiences would find Sybil's reaction to Eric's relationship with Eva strange, as class makes little difference to relationships these days.

Page 27

(1) All but 'J.B. Priestley went to university' and 'Captain Scott died in the Antarctic' should be ticked.

(2) Most married women were dependent on their husbands – Sheila would be dependent on Gerald when they married.

(3) For example, answers for Sheila might include:
- She would perhaps have had a job.
- She might have worked during WWII and become more independent.
- She would have been able to vote.

Page 28

(1) (a) Probably 1912 coal miner's strike secured minimum wage'.

(b) For example: The coal miners' strike scared wealthy businessmen like Arthur who thought they would lose profits.

(2) (a) The first point.

(b) The fact that Sybil defers to her husband is typical of the beliefs about women's place in the Edwardian era as they didn't have the vote and were seen as inferior to men.

(3) For example: there was no unemployment benefit so Sybil's charity was Eva's last hope.

Page 29

(1) (a) Paragraphs A and B match all the points. Paragraph C matches a and e.

(b) Paragraph B is the most detailed.

(2) For example: An audience in 1945 would probably have felt very sorry for Eva but may have shared Sybil's prejudice against single mothers. However, a modern audience would probably be shocked that Eva needed to rely on charity as we now have a welfare state.

Page 30

(1) For example:

Priestley presents Sybil as feeling no sense of responsibility towards the lower classes. Sybil accepts no blame for her part in Eva's death. She is presented as very judgemental.	makes a clear point about Sybil, linking her to the theme of responsibility
She pays no attention to her servant, Edna, unless it is to give her orders and shows no concern for her welfare as she tells her to wait up until she is needed. calling Eva a girl 'of that class' and looking down on her for being single and pregnant. she only helps those she feels have earned it, and feels Eva was herself to blame.	uses a key event or speech as evidence
This reflects Priestley's negative feelings about the way the rich in Edwardian society treated the working classes. Beliefs about the working class had begun to change in 1945, with the introduction of the welfare state	identifies a relevant contextual idea
an audience at that time would have been more sympathetic than Sybil about Eva's situation.	comments on audience at the time the play was written
A twenty-first century audience would certainly feel Sybil's attitude was wrong and might even see her as cruel.	compares 1945 audience with modern audience response

Unit 5

Page 34

(1) For example: Characters used to show guilt:
- Arthur and Sybil show no guilt. In Act I Arthur calls his sacking of Eva 'justified'

(2) For example: Themes and context shown:

Inspector wants each character to take responsibility:

Stands for socialist ideas about responsibility – in Act III before he leaves he talks about people being responsible for each other and 'members of one body' – reflects new ideas after WWII.

(3) Yes

Page 35

1 The guilt plan should be labelled 'Points'; the 'Sheila and Gerald' plan should be labelled 'Plot'.

2 **a** For example: theme – love, different for men and women.

b For example: *Sheila (excited): Oh – Gerald – you've got it.*

Page 36

1 **a** For example: love/morality

b Gerald, Sheila, Eric

2 **a** For example: A (exploitation) could link with a, b, c, d and e.

b For example: Exploitation can be linked to power as it was Arthur's power as a wealthy businessman that allowed him to exploit Eva for poor wages.

3 For example, in exam-style question **b**, links could draw between 'ring' and 'significance'. Annotations could include: at the end of the play Gerald thinks things can go back to how they were before; he has double-standards; he lacks a sense of social responsibility.

Page 37

1 **a** For example:

What social class does he represent? *Wealthy upper class*

How is he represented? *As pleasant at first, then as having double standards*

Does he change? *Not once he realises it was all a hoax*

What key themes does this link him to? *power, morality*

b C

2 **a** For example:

Does it link to other themes? *responsibility, morality*

Why does Priestley include the idea of power in the play? *To show how it should be used to help others.*

Which characters can be linked to power? *The Birlings and Gerald have both abused power.*

How is power shown? *a bit of both*

b For example: Priestley explores ideas about power in the play by showing how dangerous it is if it is abused and how it should be used responsibly.

Page 38

1 **a** B

b For example: *Sheila begins the play as a rather shallow character.*

c Evidence: For example: *'a pretty girl' who is 'rather excited'*

d For example: Themes: *This is the first hint in the play that love means different things to men and women.*

Unit 6

Page 42

1 For example:

Context – 'Shows inequality before welfare state and gender inequality of the time.'

Audience response – 'intended to educate original audience.'

2 For example: It links because Sheila and Eric are younger generation and Priestley wanted to show that society could be more equal.

Page 43

1

He is not intimidated by the Birlings.	✓
He represents Priestley's ideas about responsibility.	✓
He challenges the Birlings and Gerald.	✓
He isn't a real Inspector.	✗
His visit turns out to be a hoax.	✗
Edna shows him in.	✗
He exposes the family's lack of morals.	✓

2

Eva's life is difficult.	✗
Inequality allows wealthy to exploit w/class.	✓
The Birlings are wealthy.	✗
Gerald is superior to the Birlings.	✗
W/class have fewer opportunities.	✓
The Birlings benefit from inequality.	✓

Page 44

1 **a** Point 1 = E; Point 2 = B; Point 3 = D

b For example: evidence E supports Point 1 because Mrs B showed no compassion for Eva even after hearing about her fate, but the audience would be shocked.

2 For example, Point 1 with evidence E links to context as it shows how difficult life was for working classes with no welfare state.

Page 45

1 For example: B, A, C, D (this is the order the events happen in the play so it shows understanding of the structure.)

2 **a** For example: B, A and C, D (this sequence starts with the Birlings who benefit from inequality, then goes to Eva who is harmed by inequality, then on to another point about Eva and ends with ideas about how things could be different.)

b For example: B, A, C, D (this order starts with the way some people benefit from the middle classes and then moves on to those who don't.)

Page 46

1 For example: 'the stage directions describe him as creating an impression of "massiveness".'

2 Context and audience response – 'surprised an audience in 1945, as wealthy families were used to commanding respect at that time.'

3 A chronologically

Unit 7

Page 50

 For example:
- SR: 'this is shown when he talks of having learned from his business experiences'
- Interpretation: 'This all suggests that he feels his experience is valuable'
- Links: 'this all suggests'

② For example: When he calls the Inspector a 'crank' after he has left.

Page 51

① ⓐ B

ⓑ A

ⓒ C

ⓓ For example: 'even after the Inspector's visit is shown to be a hoax she insists'

② ⓐ Act II

ⓑ For example: When Arthur struggles to accept Eric was the baby's father and Sybil refuses to believe it.

Page 52

① A = c, B = b; C = a

ⓐ For example: It suggests that Sybil still treats Sheila as a child and that she feels Sheila lacks the knowledge to have a grown-up relationship with Gerald.

ⓑ For example: This suggests that Eric is beginning to make up his own mind about important issues.

Page 53

① ⓐ For example:

Priestley shows that the older generation find it difficult to understand their children:

Specific Evidence: This is shown when Sybil is shocked by Sheila using the word 'squiffy' to describe Eric's behaviour.

Interpretation: This suggests Sybil is out of touch with the younger generation and is judgemental about their way of life.

Page 54

①

key point focusing on the key words in the question	At the end of the play the relationship between Eric and his father is badly damaged.
	The relationship between Sheila and her parents is also broken by the end of the play.
specific events or speeches used as evidence	This is shown when, soon after the Inspector has left, Eric openly challenges Arthur's authority by shouting at him that they all killed Eva and Arthur responds by threatening his son
	This is made very clear after the Inspector has gone, when she responds to her father's mockery about the Inspector and the death of Eva by moving towards the door.

Interpretations that are linked to character or theme	This makes Arthur seems very aggressive and at this point the audience would realise that Arthur has learned nothing, as he is just as unpleasant as he was at the start of the play.
	This suggests she wants nothing more to do with her parents and wishes to distance herself from their views.
Phrases used to structure the interpretation - [for example…. This suggests…]	This is shown when
	This is made clear
	This suggests
	This makes

Unit 8

Page 58

Eva Smith is used by Priestley to represent the working classes and show how easily they were exploited by the wealthy.	a point that links to the question
For example, she is not seen on stage, she is only described by others.	evidence about how a character is presented
This is important as it shows how wealthy families like the Birlings rely on the working classes without ever really seeing them as real people.	interpretation
This reflects the gap between the upper and lower classes in Edwardian society.	link between interpretation and context

Eva Smith is first presented to the audience through Arthur Birling in a positive way.	a clear point
This is shown when Arthur praises her, calling her good looking and a good worker.	evidence
This suggests he thought she was a valuable employee.	interpretation
This was not unusual, as many factories liked employing women in 1912 because women could be paid less than men and were not under the protection of trade unions. This meant that if the women protested about their low pay, they could easily be sacked.	link between interpretation and context
This is shown in the play when Arthur defends his sacking of Eva, saying she had to go as she had 'too much to say'.	how context is shown in play
Gerald immediately agrees with Arthur,	extra evidence
which suggests that this lack of concern for the rights of the working classes was common at the time.	interpretation of extra evidence

Page 59

① For example: It is then shown when Sheila interrupts Arthur's suggestion that he talk to the Inspector alone. This suggests that Arthur's children are beginning to lose respect for their father and starting to think for themselves.

② For example:

Sybil Birling also abuses her power over Eva. This is shown when she admits to being prejudiced against Eva when the girl came to her for help. This is also seen when Sybil uses her power as a prominent member of the Brumley Women's Charity to stop Eva getting any support. This suggests she is hypocritical, as she presents herself as moral, but does nothing to help Eva.

Eric exploits Eva sexually. For example, when he met her in the Palace Bar he was so drunk he could have turned nasty. This is also seen when he admits he could not afterwards remember her name. This suggests he took advantage of her by force and then put her out of his mind, which implies she meant nothing to him.

Page 60

① It also suggests that Eva wanted to make herself clean again after her dealings with the Birlings, as disinfectant has connotations of killing harmful germs.

Page 61

① A

② For example:

Contextual comment: This this reflects the way middle class men in the Edwardian era would have viewed working class girls like Eva as beneath them, and felt it did not matter how badly they were treated.

Audience comment: A modern audience would find these comments very offensive as there is more gender equality these days and men are expected to treat women with respect.

Page 62

① ⓐ Evidence: 'For instance, Sheila is presented as rather childish as she still refers to her parents as 'Mummy' and 'Daddy' despite being engaged to Gerald. She is also still treated as a child by her mother, who answers for her when she doesn't reply to Gerald's question about being part of the family.'

ⓑ Additional interpretation: 'It also suggests that Sybil is concerned about impressing Gerald as he is considered to be a good catch for Sheila.'

ⓒ Flows clearly: 'This reflects the traditional view that young people should respect and obey their elders, and this would have been even more expected at the time the play was set.'

② For example: He is threatening towards his mother when he learns she refused to help Eva; he laughs at his father's worries that his knighthood is lost.

Unit 9

Page 66

① For example: 'committed', 'unease', 'qualms'

② For example: 'and', 'while', 'when'

③ For example: For example, her first speech is directed to be spoken 'gaily'. It is also supposed to be said 'possessively'.

④ For example:

Idea 1: Love is shown to be damaging to Eva.

Idea 2: Arthur sees the marriage as a business match, not a love match.

Idea 3: Love is seen differently by men and women.

Page 67

①

Arthur Birling speaks about the engagement and his business hopes. *arranged*	Gerald talks about saving Eva from Alderman Meggarty. *squalid*	Eric says he insisted on going back to Eva's lodgings for sex. *sordid*
Gerald defends his lack of attention to Sheila over the summer. *dishonest*	Gerald says Eva loved him and he was the most important person in her life. *fairy tale*	Eric says he did not love Eva 'or anything'. *exploitative*
Sybil Birling warns Sheila that men will always put business first. *unequal*	Sheila returns Gerald's engagement ring. *commitment*	Gerald asks Sheila to take the ring back as 'Everything's all right now.' *hypocritical*

②

He tells the Birlings that Eva died 'after several hours of agony'. *compassionate/ judgemental*	Sheila warns her mother that the Inspector knows everything. *omniscient*	He warns the Birlings that everybody has a responsibility to care for each other. *prophetic/ symbolic*
He interrupts Arthur Birling's impatient protest: 'cutting through, massively'. *powerful/ formidable*	Sybil Birling says he has made a big impression on the younger generation. *commanding/ imposing*	His visit proves to be a hoax. *mysterious/ symbolic*

Page 68

① When, whereas

② For example:

ⓐ The Inspector questions each of the family in turn *in order to* build up a 'chain of events' that will make them consider their behaviour.

ⓑ The Inspector challenges Arthur over his treatment of Eva, *but* Arthur tries to justify his decision to dismiss her.

ⓒ Sheila believes in the idea of romantic love at the start of the play, *whereas* she is more realistic at the end when she refuses to take back Gerald's ring.

Page 69

1 **a** Sybil Birling insists the Inspector do his duty and find the father of Eva's child.

b Sybil Birling insists the Inspector do his duty, because she thinks the child's father is to blame.

c Sybil Birling insists the Inspector do his duty, believing that the father of Eva's baby is to blame rather than her.

d Sybil Birling insists the Inspector do his duty, which is ironic as the father is Eric.

2 **a** The Inspector takes his duties very seriously, encouraging the audience to see him as having high moral standards.

b Sybil Birling is rude to the Inspector and says his comments are 'impertinent' which creates the impression that she is arrogant.

Page 70

1 For example:

a / b good [powerful, formidable, impressive]; bothered [intimidated, phased, overawed]; stays [remains]; big [important, significant]

c / d

> At the start of the play the Inspector is presented as a <u>powerful</u> character as he is described in the stage directions as giving an impression of 'massiveness' and he is not <u>intimidated</u> by Arthur Birling's boasting about being Mayor. Arthur gets impatient with him and Gerald gets annoyed, whereas the Inspector <u>remains</u> cool and speaks 'gravely'. He also interrupts Arthur, demanding Arthur tell him what he did to Eva, which suggests the Inspector is going to be a <u>significant</u> character in the play.

Notes

Notes

Notes

Notes

Notes